RUN, BABY, RUN

What Every Owner, Breeder & Handicapper
Should Know About Lasix® in Racehorses

Bill Heller

THE RUSSELL MEERDINK COMPANY, LTD.
Neenah, Wisconsin

ISBN 0-929346-71-8

Library of Congress Cataloging-in-Publication Data

Heller, Bill.
    Run, baby, run : what every owner, breeder & handicapper should know about Lasix in racehorses / Bill Heller.
      p. cm.
    ISBN 0-929346-71-8
    1. Furosemide--Physiological effect. 2. Veterinary drugs. 3. Race horses--Effect of drugs on. I. Title.

    SF918.F87 H45 2002
    636.089'51--dc21

2002075182

Published by

The Russell Meerdink Company, Ltd.
1555 South Park Ave.
Neenah, WI 54956
(920) 725-0955 Worldwide • (800) 635-6499 U.S. & Canada
www.horseinfo.com

*To the Hambletonian Society
for running Lasix-free stakes races since 1991.*

Also by Bill Heller

Obsession: Bill Musselman's Relentless Quest

Overlay, Overlay

The Will to Win: The Ron Turcotte Story

*Playing Tall — The Ten Shortest
Players in NBA History*

Harness Overlays

*Travelin' Sam, America's
Sports Ambassador*

Exotic Overlays

Billy Haughton — The Master

Turf Overlays

Thoroughbred Legends: Go For Wand

Thoroughbred Legends: Forego

Thoroughbred Legends: Personal Ensign

Graveyard of Champions

4

Acknowledgments

So many kind people helped me with this book, I'm not sure where to begin. Two people I had never met, Scot Waterman, the Executive Director of the NTRA Racing Integrity and Drug Task Force, and racing writer Pete Selin in Texas, were incredibly valuable, not only in providing me with important information. Scot helped translate the frequently indecipherable scientific jargon of dozens of studies, went out of his way to update each state's medication policy, and patiently answered all of my questions — and there were lots of them. Pete sent me crucial articles which allowed me to construct a time-line of Lasix use in America. His dad, Gerard, was also gracious and helpful.

Scot Waterman's predecessor with the NTRA, my buddy Jim Gallagher who is now with the New York Racing Association, helped steer me in the right direction on several issues.

My dear friend with the Hambletonian Society and Breeders Crown, Moira Fanning, the president of the United States Harness Writers Association, not only provided information and phone numbers, but helped me compile Lasix information by counting dozens of races herself. Why am I not surprised? Her boss, Tom Charters, the CEO of the Hambletonian Society and Breeders Crown, searched through minutes of old meetings to send me information. Bob Heyden of The Meadowlands went through all the trouble of researching three weeks of racing from three different years at The Meadowlands to help me understand how Lasix is used in harness racing.

Cheryl Buley, a member of the New York State Racing and

Wagering Board, gave me a great lead on Lasix alternatives, and Stacy Walker, the Board's Public Information Officer, was great, too, as usual.

My co-contributor to *The Backstretch* magazine, Neil Morrice in England, ran down phone numbers of English trainers and passed them on.

Reaching Andre Fabre in France was a collaborative effort involving my good friend at the NTRA, Joan Lawrence, Andy Byrnes of the New York Racing Association Racing Office and Adrian Beaumont of the International Racing Bureau.

Gwen Weldy at the Albany College of Pharmacy was a tremendous help in amassing studies done on Lasix since 1967. Allan Reney of the New York State Library Reference Desk was also helpful.

Cathy Schenck of the Keeneland Library dug up dozens of newspaper and magazine articles about Lasix which were crucial to the book.

Several research scientists not only did interviews, but also sent me dozens of studies, which were of great value. They included Dr. Larry Soma at the University of Pennsylvania, Dr. George Maylin of Cornell University, California veterinarian Dr. Rick Arthur, Dr. Kenneth Hinchcliff of Ohio State University and Dr. Tom Tobin of the University of Kentucky.

Eva Waters and the staff at the Association of Racing Commissioners International, Sally Baker and the staff at the American Association of Equine Practitioners, and Debbie Hernandez at the *Daily Racing Form* were all very helpful.

Thanks to Dr. Ted Hill, Dr. Neil Cleary, Dave Hicks, Terry Meyocks and Barry Schwartz at the New York Racing Association.

Thanks to Rena Elswick of the Kentucky Racing Commission.

Washington Post/Daily Racing Form columnist Andy Beyer did a lengthy interview which was of great importance in tracing Lasix's history.

Thanks to Dr. Warrick Bayly, Dr. Marvin Beeman, Stan

Bergstein, Dr. Jerry Bilinski, Gary Biszantz, Dr. Jerry Black, Elliott Burch, Neil Drysdale, Andre Fabre, Mike Flynn, Alan Foreman, Ebby Gerry, John Gosden, Seth Hancock, Dr. Alex Harthill, Allen Jerkens, Phil Johnson, John Kimmel, Doug Koch, Mike Levine, Ben Liebman, Dr. Kenneth McKeever, John McLain, Lou Mettinis, Gasper Moschera, Dr. Rainer Muser, John Nerud, Ben Nolt, Jr., Dr. Joe O'Dea, Dinny Phipps, Lonny Powell, Rob Rose, Geoffrey Russell, Dr. Rick Sams, Rick Schosberg, Lauren Stich, Don Swick, Buzz Tenney and Tom Ventura. All your interviews contributed significantly to this book.

Also thanks to Joe Flood and Craig Shoemaker of CNS.

My wife, Anna, and my son, Benjamin, helped in numerous ways and put up with me spending half my life in my den. So did our dog Belle Mont.

To anyone I've neglected to thank specifically, I apologize.

Publisher's Note

Lasix® is a registered trademark owned by Intervet, Inc. for the drug furosemide. In June 2001, Intervet announced the Lasix® (furosemide) manufactured for equine use had been renamed Salix™. As of the publication date of this book, racetracks throughout the United States and Canada, the *Daily Racing Form* and other racing publications and horsemen everywhere continue to use the term Lasix®. Thus, the term Lasix will be used in the discussion of furosemide for equine use.

Table of Contents

Chapter 1

More Questions Than Answers

The veterinarian drove his truck past the security gate and onto the busy backstretch of the racetrack. He parked at one of the barns, got out, opened the back of his truck and took out a syringe. A stable hand showed him the Thoroughbred who would be racing that afternoon, one who had been certified as a bleeder. The horse hadn't gushed blood through his nostrils. Few racehorses do. But almost all incur bleeding in their respiratory tracts from the strenuous demands of racing.

In the United States, and in only seven other countries in the world, this horse was eligible, on the day he was to race, to receive an injection of the controversial medication Lasix, a potent diuretic whose equine version was re-named Salix in June, 2001. The veterinarian found a vein in the horse's neck and injected five cc. of Lasix. The horse did not move. The procedure took five seconds.

It had to be quick. There were dozens of other Thoroughbreds waiting for their shot of Lasix that day, four hours or less before they'd break from the starting gate.

It is routine, so routine that in 2001 more than 92 percent of American Thoroughbreds raced on Lasix at tracks around the country in a national sample of more than 48,000 starters. In two states, Kentucky and California, the percentages were even higher. Standardbreds average about half as much, although the numbers are increasing.

Yet more than three decades after Lasix was introduced to

the backstretches of America's racetracks, heated debate about the medication persists.

• Does it stop bleeding? A mountain of scientific evidence says it does not, though it may greatly diminish bleeding in some horses.

• Does it improve a horse's performance? This is a non-issue. Some horses improve their performances dramatically, as one would expect from the weight loss. Horses quickly urinate as much as 25 pounds after Lasix is administered.

• Can Lasix mask other drugs by diluting them? Studies more than 25 years ago showed that it did.

• Why are the United States, Canada, Argentina, Brazil, Chile, Mexico, Saudi Arabia and Venezuela the only countries in the world allowing Lasix on race day? Is the rest of the world wrong?

• Why did 21 of the 24 racing jurisdictions which voted to remove Lasix from the National Association of State Racing Commissioners' non-binding, medication guidelines in 1982 restore Lasix within three years? The NASRC, now known as the Association of State Racing Commissioners International, didn't put Lasix back into its medication guidelines until 1996. Why did it wait 14 years?

The racing industry has been in deep denial about Lasix since Day One.

Lasix, generically known as furosemide, was supposed to help bleeders, enabling horses to race more frequently. Instead, the average number of starts for Thoroughbreds is down significantly. In 2000, average field size (8.11) and average starts per runner (7.10) were all-time lows, according to the Jockey Club. In 2001, average starts per runner dropped even lower to 6.97. A 30-year precipitous decline began in the 1970s, right about the time Lasix began being used. In 1970, the average field size was 8.62 and the average starts per runner were 10.22.

Claiborne Farm President Seth Hancock sees Lasix as one

of the causes. "I've talked about this until I'm blue in my face, and obviously nobody's listening," he said. "We'll keep seeing horses make fewer and fewer starts every year and weakening the breed."

Lasix advocates say that not using Lasix would be cruel to horses who bleed, but those questioning Lasix's blanket usage are not advocating the wholesale elimination of a drug widely regarded as useful and safe, only to ban its use on race day, and/or its use on two-year-olds and/or its over-use. Are Hall of Fame trainers John Nerud and Elliott Burch cruel because they advocate no race-day medication?

Under Nerud's lead, on Nov. 23, 1999, the New York Thoroughbred Breeders, Inc., Board of Directors unanimously approved a proposal by Nerud — then vice-president of the NYTB — that Thoroughbreds everywhere receive no medication within 72 hours of a race.

The NYTB was not being delusional. Its Board did not expect the rest of the Thoroughbred industry to embrace the proposal. "When we came out and made that statement, we were more interested in making a statement and taking a stand on the situation," former NYTB President Mike Flynn said. "And it did get someone's attention. We got a lot of support from some areas and were highly criticized from others. But, as a result, it was the beginning of a hard look at medication in our state and other states. So I think it served a purpose."

The Lasix epidemic in North America does not. It is of dubious value to the sports of Thoroughbred and Standardbred racing in the United States and raises unsettling questions, none more important than this: What else is Lasix doing?

Has Lasix become more than a medication in the United States? Are trainers, owners, veterinarians and racing commissions so wrapped up in the concept of immediate gratification that they are neglecting the welfare of the Thoroughbred?

The issue is not whether first-time Lasix improves performance, but rather: how much does it improve performance and which horses does it improve? The *Daily Racing Form* does not provide every trainer's record with first-time Lasix horses under the horses' past performance lines just for the heck of it.

This isn't rocket science. Simply open the *Form* any day.

Buddha, the winner of the 2002 Wood Memorial, made his career debut without Lasix in a seven-furlong maiden race at Belmont Park, Oct. 22, 2001. He was 10th by 18 lengths at 18-1. His second career start was in a seven-furlong maiden race at Gulfstream Park with Lasix, Feb. 9, 2002. He won by 4 1/4 lengths at 2-1, as his Beyer Speed Figure rocketed from 47 to 96.

Stylish Sultan made his first two career starts in five and a half furlong, two-year-old maiden races at Rockingham Park. Without Lasix, he was eighth by 26 1/4 lengths at 36-1, Sept. 10, 2001. Just a week later with Lasix, he won by a neck at 11-1. Without Lasix, he went five and a half furlongs in 1:11 3/5. With it, his time was 1:08.

True Direction, a three-year-old in 2002, made his first two starts in six furlong maiden races at Aqueduct. In his debut without Lasix, Feb. 3, he was fourth by 3 1/2 lengths at 26-1, getting six furlongs in 1:13 3/5. With Lasix in his next start, March 3, he won by 12 lengths at 3-1 in 1:10 2/5. His Beyer jumped from 59 to 106.

Green Jeans debuted without Lasix, Dec. 22, 2001, at Aqueduct in a six furlong maiden race and finished ninth by 35 1/4 lengths at 68-1. He added Lasix for his second career start, a seven-furlong maiden race at Aqueduct, March 23, 2002, and won by 6 1/2 lengths at 16-1. His Beyer went from -0 to 74.

There are similar examples every day at every racetrack in the country. There are also daily examples of horses whose performance did not change or even regressed with the addition of Lasix. Discerning which horses will step up on first-time Lasix is difficult, though it appears to be the most effective on front-runners who have been tiring late.

A table of more than 400 Thoroughbred trainers and their two-year percentages with first-time Lasix horses appears later in this book.

There are other important questions left unanswered. Can Lasix flush other drugs out of a horse's system or mask them by diluting them?

"Yes, absolutely," said Jim Gallagher, former Executive Director of the National Thoroughbred Racing Association Racing Integrity and Drug Task Force. "If Lasix is given in a large dose or a dose close to a race, that sample will be diluted."

The American Association of Equine Practitioners justified approval of Lasix in the early 1980s with guidelines of dose and time of administration, but the reality is that 20 years later, six racing states allow double the recommended dose and six others do not even specify a dose. What good are guidelines if they're not followed?

Is Lasix more potent when used in conjunction with other drugs, say phenylbutazone (Bute) and/or clenbuterol? In early March of 2002, the Maryland Racing Commission directed its racetracks to note "adjunct" medications used with Lasix in track programs. Those drugs included blood-clotting agents and medication used to treat high blood pressure. Louisiana and Kentucky allow the use of adjunct drugs with Lasix, too.

There is scientific research, however, that the use of Lasix with other drugs might be dangerous for horses.

And what does Lasix do to two-year-olds? When an entire field of two-year-old first time starters debut on Lasix, isn't something terribly out of whack? Pennsylvania and Michigan prohibit Lasix for two-year-old Thoroughbreds and Standardbreds.

"You look at those first-time starters on Lasix as two-year-olds, and somebody is cheating," Dinny Phipps, Chairman of the Jockey Club, said. "Either the owner, the veterinarian or the trainer. Someone is not telling the truth. There are just not that many bleeders that are first-time starters. They're getting away with something, and it's not fair to the game."

Why does the percentage of two-year-old Thoroughbreds

using Lasix in 2001 range from 28 to 56 percent in most racing jurisdictions and hover at 80 percent in Kentucky and California? California is where 622 of 636 Thoroughbreds racing at Del Mar from July 18 through 29 were on Lasix. That's 97.8 percent, lower than the one for Bute. Every one of 636 starters raced on Bute.

Kentucky is an interesting state, one that requires Standardbreds to be certified by veterinarians as bleeders to receive Lasix while allowing Thoroughbreds to be treated with Lasix by having their trainers simply request it when they enter their horses. "We do not deal with demonstrative bleeding in this state," Bernie Hettel, executive director of the Kentucky Racing Commission, said May 7, 2002.

But Kentucky does allow multiple therapeutic medications on racing day, a policy which has generated considerable debate among Kentucky's own horsemen.

In a Kentucky Horsemen's Benevolent and Protective Association survey of its 6,000 members in 2002, 91.8 percent of 724 responses supported Kentucky's current medication policy, correctly referred to by the *Daily Racing Form*'s Matt Hegarty as the most permissive in the country. An accompanying letter with the survey from then KHBPA President Dr. Alex Harthill asked voters who opposed the medication policy "to take another look" before doing the survey. "Kentucky's medication policy, like that of the Olympics, assures a level playing field, relying on science to insure the health and welfare of the equine athlete in conjunction with the integrity of the game," Harthill wrote.

Then why did the Board of Directors of the Kentucky Thoroughbred Association respond immediately with an open letter disclosing its disagreement with the results of the KHBPA poll and its "dissatisfaction" with the current medication policies in Kentucky?

And why is a Kentucky breeding operation as prestigious as Claiborne Farm cutting back its involvement in racing? "The last two years we've put anywhere from 25 to 30 two-year-olds in training," Seth Hancock said. "This year it's about 18. Next year will be 10 or 12. It's a combination of things, but the medication policy is one of the reasons. I'm not a vet and I'm not a trainer, so maybe I'm not qualified to comment, but I don't understand the point of starting two-year-olds on Lasix. If they're bleeding, they should be given more time. I understand after a time or two or three, a horse may need it, but I sure don't understand first-time starters on it."

Across the country, another prominent horseman questioned the wisdom of Lasix's unfettered use and its potential consequences.

"Personally, I'm someone who favors less rather than more," said Gary Biszantz, a long-time California owner and breeder at Cobra Farm who was elected Chairman of the Board of Trustees of the Thoroughbred Owners and Breeders Association, Aug. 10, 2001. "I just think that horses can need some assistance, and we should be able to do the things that are humane for them and help them. But on race days, in my judgment, horses should probably run clean and free of medication."

They used to run that way on Thoroughbred racing's day of champions, the Breeders' Cup. In 2001, the Breeders' Cup at Belmont Park was the Bleeders' Cup. Ninety-one of 95 starters in the Breeders' Cup raced on Lasix. That included 23 of 24 two-year-olds who competed in the Juvenile and Juvenile Filly. The previous time the Breeders' Cup was held in New York in 1995 — the first year Lasix was allowed on race day in New York — 47 of 81 horses used Lasix and just seven of 21 two-year-olds. And why did most European horses, who did not use Lasix on race-day in Europe, use it for the 2001 Breeders' Cup?

Why in harness racing's equivalent of the Breeders' Cup, the Breeders Crown, did only two of 156 two-year-olds race on Lasix the last four years?

Why has the number of three-year-olds racing on Lasix in Thoroughbred racing's most gloried stakes, the Kentucky Derby, climbed from five-of-16 in 1990 to 17-of-17 in 2001? There hasn't been a Lasix-free horse in the Derby since 1998. Is that progress?

Why is Lasix, as well as Butazolidin, not allowed in Standardbred racing's most gloried stakes for three-year-old trotters, the Hambletonian and Hambletonian Oaks? How could all 43 trotters who competed in the two stakes in 2001, including elimination heats, survive without Lasix? The Hambletonian and Hambletonian Oaks have been Lasix and Bute free since 1991. "The Board of Directors wanted to make a statement about medication," Tom Charters, CEO of the Hambletonian Society and of the Breeders Crown, said.

Despite that message, Lasix use in Standardbreds is increasing. Why? And why is Lasix usage disproportionately high on weekends when higher purse races are contested?

"More trainers are using it, and I presume they're using it for the same reason a lot of Thoroughbred trainers use it, because everybody else is," Stan Bergstein, executive vice-president of Harness Tracks of America, said. "I believe the sport would be better off without it."

How did Lasix evolve from a therapeutic medication, whose original animal use was to treat mild heart attacks in cats and dogs, to a designer drug for racehorses?

Are we masking a horse's physical problems with Lasix instead of treating them? If that is true, what are the consequences when we breed such horses?

"To me, it's very bad for the breed, for racing and for the image of racing," French trainer Andre Fabre said. "I find it very interesting that good American horses go to Dubai and race without Lasix."

If America's best horses can race without Lasix in million-dollar stakes races in Dubai, why do they race on Lasix in million-dollar stakes races in the United States on Breeders' Cup Day?

How is this for racing's image? Verne Winchell's Fleet Renee, trained by Michael Dickinson, was one of the top three-year-old fillies of 2001. After she won the $250,000 Grade 1 Mother Goose Stakes at Belmont Park, June 30th, it was discovered that she raced with an overage of Lasix. In New York, that means a lot of Lasix since New York's maximum dose of 10 cc. (500 milligrams) is double that of most other states.

Dickinson was fined just $250 by the New York State Racing and Wagering Board because it was his first overage in New York. Dickinson appealed the fine, and the Board, after conducting a hearing on the matter, dismissed his appeal on June 12, 2002.

Fleet Renee was not disqualified and the purse money from the Mother Goose Stakes was not redistributed. That left Winchell with the winner's share of $150,000, which can cover a lot of $250 fines.

Does that promote a sense of integrity? "We have to make sure the patron thinks the game is honest," Dinny Phipps said. "The patron deserves honesty."

And what do our horses deserve?

Has the American racing industry fully evaluated alternatives to Lasix, including the nasal strip, nebulizers, other medications, dietary herbal supplements and a better barn environment for horses?

At the American Association of Equine Practitioners historic Racehorse Medication Summit at the annual University of Arizona Racing Symposium, Dec. 4, 2001, racing's industry leaders were tripping over themselves complimenting each other for finally beginning to consider the idea of uniform medication rules throughout the country, a concept other countries embraced decades ago. In doing so, the leaders hinted that, maybe, a drug policy prohibiting every medication except Lasix on race day could be an intelligent direction to pursue.

But why should Lasix be exempted?

Timing is crucial. If Lasix is grandfathered in now, it may be with our racehorses forever.

That might be okay with most veterinarians, who have

developed a cottage industry by charging trainers/owners for endoscopic examinations and then injecting nearly every Thoroughbred and every other Standardbred in North America with Lasix and charging for that, too. Then trainers and owners must pay for electrolytes which must be given to the dehydrated, Lasix-using horse after the race.

In addressing Lasix, the Thoroughbred and Standardbred racing industry has exhibited a callous disregard for the bettor. It took years before each horse's medication information was indicated on track programs and years more until it was included in the *Daily Racing Form*. In harness racing, charts in The Meadowlands program in 2001 did not indicate which horses raced on Lasix.

Racing fans are used to such treatment, but what of the general public that tunes into the Kentucky Derby and is asked to deal with medication issues such as first-time Lasix? What kind of image are we sending out?

"I don't think the public recognizes the difference between Lasix and heroin," said Dr. Doug Koch, a veterinarian who owns Berkshire Stud in Pine Plains, New York, and co-bred 2002 Arkansas Derby winner Private Emblem. "A horse is either on drugs or not. When you watch the Breeders' Cup and you hear them talk about first time Lasix, it's a tremendous detriment to the sport. Having horses run on medication taints the sport. I think it's driving owners out of the game."

When New York State, the last bastion of hay, oats and water, caved into pressure and legalized Lasix in 1995, the argument was that it would create a level playing field.

Thoroughbred racing has indeed created a level playing field in America, a level of race-day drug dependency never seen before in racing history. Standardbred racing isn't far behind.

Chapter 2

Bleeding

Horses have bled after strenuous exercise for centuries, but only left physical evidence in the most severe cases: when they bled through their nostrils. Humans assumed that the bleeding originated there. It did not.

In an article published in 1974 after studying bleeders in England, Dr. W. Robert Cook suggested that a horse's bleeding originated in the lung, and that exercise precipitated this bleeding.

The invention of the fiberoptic endoscope soon afterwards confirmed Cook's theory. The fiberoptic endoscope is a long, soft and flexible tube inserted through the horse's nostril and into his respiratory tract. In the tube are two bundles of light-carrying, glass fibers which illuminate the interior of the respiratory tract and transmit the image back to the veterinarian. For the first time, veterinarians could actually see blood in a horse's trachea.

Consequently, horses who had been stopping in their raccs before the advent of the fiberoptic endoscope may have had a legitimate reason. "In the old days, they didn't have the scope," said John Gosden, who has trained Thoroughbreds in England and in Southern California. "Therefore, horses who were accused of not trying, of being hanging dogs, may well have been bleeding. It's obviously painful for a horse."

In part two of her superbly crafted, five-part series about Lasix in *The Blood-Horse*, July 27th, 1985, Deirdre Biles reported that Markham, a Turf historian, wrote in the late 1500s, "Many horses, especially young horses, are oft subject to this bleeding at the nose."

Yet a bleeder who never raced became one of the most important sires in Thoroughbred racing history.

Originally called Young Childers, Bleeding Childers got his nickname for the obvious reason and never raced, though his full brother, Flying Childers, was undefeated in a racing career which began in 1721.

Bleeding Childers was sold to Mr. Bartlet of Nuttle Court near Masham, Yorkshire, and re-named Bartlet's (also spelled Bartlett's) Childers. Send to stud, he became the great-grand sire of the pre-eminent Thoroughbred foundation sire Eclipse, the horse from which 80 percent of all modern Thoroughbreds trace their parentage.

In a 1990 presentation to the American Association of Equine Practitioners, California veterinarian Dr. Rick Arthur, who would become president of the AAEP in 1997, cited this West German literary reference to Bleeding Childers' impact on the Thoroughbred breed:

"BARTLETTS CHILDERS (BLEEDING CHILDERS), an untried blood-vessel breaker (!), enlarged the fountain head created by the greatest prepotent Arabians ... It was Bartlett's Childers who was the first stallion to teach breeders that the untried racer was perfectly fit and able to sire the best of racehorses. Needless to say, there was but little racing more than two centuries ago. Of course, there were other untried horses at stud, and yet there was no other progenitor of comparable impact on the entire breed."

Bleeding Childers bled at his nostrils, a condition called epistaxis, which continues to this day, but occurs infrequently.

The New York Racing Association keeps records of horses who actually bled through their nostrils after a race. In 2001, there were eight out of a total of 18,927 starters. Of those 18,927 starters in New York that year, 16,200 (85.6 percent) raced on Lasix.

A five-year, retrospective study of 247,564 Thoroughbreds and 4,045 Anglo-Arabian starters in Japan from 1992 through 1997 found that only .15 percent suffered epistaxis. The study concluded: "The higher frequency in shorter races suggests that higher intensity exercise of shorter duration may increase the probability of EIPH."[1]

One of the first researchers to study bleeding in horses' lungs was Dr. John Pascoe at the University of California-Davis School of Veterinary Medicine. Pascoe used the fiberoptic endoscope, which allowed a much better view of the source of the bleeding, and coined the term of exercise-induced pulmonary hemorrhaging. That acronym, EIPH, has been used ever since.

Naming it has been easier than explaining it.

Horses are not the only mammals to suffer EIPH, which has been observed in greyhound dogs, racing camels, and human beings, mostly swimmers, divers and high-altitude climbers. Horses, however, have the highest incidence of EIPH, not just racehorses — including Thoroughbreds, Standardbreds, Quarter Horses and steeplechasers — but draft horses, polo ponies and horses that compete in performance events such as barrel racing, cutting and roping, cross country events and show jumping.

Why do horses bleed in their lungs?

"It's an occupational hazard of fast, intense racing in horses," Arthur said in March, 2002. "This has been a problem from the time they began racing horses."

Writing in the magazine *Horsepower-Ireland*, veterinary surgeon Des Groome suggested a possible cause: "The root of the problem, I believe, lies in evolution. The primitive wild horse evolved in herds as a Savannah grazer. Being a herbivore and open to predators, the horse was genetically programmed with a fight or flight instinct to recognize danger and flee predators by accelerating rapidly to gallop over short distances at top speed. In a survival of the fittest scenario, the fittest could shake off a wild cat after a few furlongs.

---

[1] T. Takahasi, A. Hiraga, H. Ohmura, M. Kai and J.H. Jones, *Journal of the American Veterinary Medical Association*, May, 2001

"Long miles in selective grazing were traveled the rest of the time by the horse at a leisurely, energy-saving back canter. A few hundred years of breeding for racing thus cannot reverse the unnatural demands made on horses' lungs by the equine sports we have devised. In simple terms, it's just not natural to gallop, jump and race at the modern pace, over two, three, four miles or more. We must accept these as unchangeable factors."

Laura Phelps-Bell, an equine teacher and instructor for more than 25 years, offered a similar theory on her web site, Ask Laura Phelps-Bell: "From an evolutionary standpoint, horses were designed to graze and travel for miles and miles at a walking pace and only would sprint if trying to escape a predator. Their hearts and lungs were not designed for extended periods of hard running or for repeated sprints. What we as humans may be asking them to do goes completely against how evolution has designed them."

In his book, *Specifications for Speed in the Racehorse — The Airflow Factors*, Dr. W. Robert Cook suggests that Thoroughbreds' and Standardbreds' airways were not designed in such a manner either, and postulates that 95 percent of Thoroughbreds and Standardbreds have some restriction of their airways.

Cook emphasizes that since horses, unlike humans and greyhounds, breathe only through their nose, they require a maximum supply of oxygen which is more easily supplied if the nasal cavity, throat and voice box are able to open as widely as possible. "My research has shown that there is a strong statistical relationship between a horse's racing ability and its airflow characteristics as judged by width of jaw and health of voice box," he wrote.

His contention has been known to sharp horsemen for decades. Harness racing driver/trainer Billy Haughton, considered by many as the finest horseman of the 20th Century, probably looked at more yearlings than anyone in racing history. He personally inspected every yearling at a sale, and he attended many sales during his Hall of Fame career, keeping copious details in sales catalogs.

Haughton, who also owned dozens of Thoroughbreds during his life, was smart enough to use helpful information wherever he could find it. Thus, in the chapter he wrote about yearling selection in *The Care and Training of the Trotter and Pacer*, a bible for harness horsemen for decades, he said, "Some years ago I read that the late (Hall of Fame Thoroughbred trainer) Sunny Jim Fitzimmons said he always wanted to be able to get four fingers between the jaws of any yearling he ever bought. He said that if he couldn't do that, they didn't have sufficient space there for proper air intake. I have been practicing this myself for a number of years now and I have found it to be generally true. I have marked this in my catalog for quite a few years, and in checking back, I haven't found a single horse that failed this 'finger test' that ever amounted to anything more than an ordinary raceway horse."

There are many theories about why horses bleed. Incredibly, though, despite more than 25 years of research, there is no definitive answer.

An analysis in the Jan. 1, 2001 *Horse Report*[2] and a series of studies by Dr. Pascoe and Dr. Jim Jones of the Cal-Davis School of Veterinary Medicine[3] showed that the pressures in a horse's heart are unusually high, thus raising the blood pressure throughout the lung and setting up conditions which might induce EIPH.

Additional collaborative studies with the Japan Racing Association using surgically implanted catheters in conjunction with ultrasound crystals surgically affixed to the surface of the heart, directly measured the mechanics of the heart during exercise. Those studies showed that the fundamental cause of the high pressure in the heart, and hence the lungs, appears to be the heart's inability to relax quickly enough between beats during extreme

---

[2] University of California-Davis Center for Equine Health, Horse Report, January 1, 2001
[3] These studies were funded by the Grayson-Jockey Club and Cal-Davis Center for Equine Health

exercise. When the heart is not relaxed and too stiff, it takes higher pressure in the lungs to fill the heart between beats.

Dr. Jones and several colleagues wanted to study why the horse's heart relaxes too slowly at maximum exercise, and selected another athletic mammal to study: the pronghorn antelope, that has one of the highest abilities to utilize oxygen and is capable of sprinting at nearly 60 miles per hour and running for an extended period of time at 45 miles per hour. Jones's studies showed that although the pronghorn is more aerobic and pumps relatively more blood than the horse, it does so without the high blood pressures that occur in the horse. This may mean that body and heart size may be an important factor in understanding why horses' lungs bleed.

Progress has been made in determining exactly where in the lungs horses bleed. In a 2001 presentation about EIPH at the World Equine Airways Society (WEAS) Conference in Edinburgh, Scotland, Dr. David Marlin of the Centre for Equine Studies, Animal Health Trust, Newmarket, said, "In nearly all horses, the damage initially occurs in the very tips of the right and left dorsal-caudal (uppermost and rear) part of the lung."

A summary of theories explaining EIPH was also discussed at the same conference by Dr. Kenneth Hinchcliff, a Professor at the College of Veterinary Medicine at Ohio State University. The 46-year-old native of Australia concluded: "It is likely that the pathogenesis of EIPH involves several processes including stress failure of pulmonary capillaries, small airway disease and intrathoracic shear forces generated during running."

A 2000 study by four researchers at Kansas State University[4] suggested, "In the exercising horse, a pulmonary arterial pressure threshold exists above which hemorrhage occurs, and that pressure is often exceeded during high speed sprint exercise."

---

[4] I. Langsetmo, M. Fedde, T. Meyer and H. Erickson, "Relationship of Pulmonary Arterial Pressure to Pulmonary Haemorrhage in Exercising Horses," Equine Veterinary Journal (2000)

EIPH may cause permanent alterations in the blood supply to the affected parts of the lung and/or inflammation in the lung. Repeated incidences of EIPH may cause structural changes in the lung.

At the 2001 Scotland Conference, Professor Ron Slocombe of the University of Melbourne said, "Inflammation resolves only slowly after an episode of EIPH, and weeks to months may elapse before the affected lung returns to normal — providing bouts of strenuous exercise are discontinued."

Hinchcliff added, "Periodic rest, on pasture, may help the lung recover from escalating trauma."

Instead, horses with EIPH are raced a week or two later, thanks to Lasix.

Chapter 3

Lasix, er, Salix

Through the years, remedies for bleeding horses included placing pennies in horses' water buckets and wrapping copper around their tails, Deirdre B. Biles wrote in her 1985 *Blood-Horse* series on Lasix. She said other remedies included a mixture of oxalic and malonic acids or vitamin K, both of which were used to enhance the blood's clotting ability, and conjugated estrogens and citrus bioflavinoids to reduce capillary and venous bleeding during surgery.

But the most popular medication for bleeding in horses was one originally targeted for, and is still used on, human beings.

Lasix was unveiled for human use as a diuretic earlier in the 1960s. It increases the volume on urine produced by the kidneys and causes excess fluid in the tissues to decrease. In doing so, it takes out electrolytes, potassium and sodium and lowers the water content of blood, lowering blood pressure and making it easier for the heart to work.

In 1967, Hoechst Roussel Veterinary, originally known as National Laboratories, then as American Hoechst Corp., introduced Lasix, calling it the "pioneer furosemide product." Lasix was approved as a medication for dogs, cats and horses which are not used for food by the Food and Drug Administration in 1967. "It was approved as a diuretic to induce urination," Dr. Rainer Muser said. "In the process of doing that, it was determined it could be used for cats and dogs with low-grade heart failure. It could control the situation. That's the medical use of it." Muser was a director of research and development with the Hoechst Corp. in Frankfort, Germany, and then worked for the company in the United States.

Specifically, the FDA approved Lasix for horses to treat edema, an abnormal accumulation of fluid in cells, tissues or cavities of the body resulting in swelling.

On June 1, 2001, Intervet, which had acquired Hoechst Roussel, announced from its headquarters in Millsboro, Delaware, that the equine drug Lasix had been re-named Salix, and that Hoechst Roussel, which has since become Aventis Pharmaceuticals, Inc., would continue to manufacture and sell the human drug Lasix under that name.

The horse industry, never noted for quick acceptance of change, has been slow to embrace a new name for a product that has been around for more than three decades.

This apparently frustrates people who work at Intervet. One of them suggested that calling Salix "Lasix" was not only wrong but could lead to an investigation by the Food and Drug Administration.

Thus let it be known: The equine version of Lasix is now properly known as Salix. It is also known by the generic term furosemide.

So how exactly did Salix become the most popular medication to treat exercise-induced pulmonary hemorrhaging in horses? "As far as the use in horses, I have not the foggiest idea of how it started," Muser said. "It was used in different ways. That all evolved over the years. I was just an observer on the sideline."

Since Salix is being injected into hundreds of thousands of horses, maybe it would be wise to know how the company that produces Salix sees its medication.

On its website, Intervet advertises SALIX (furosemide) as "A diuretic-saluretic for prompt relief of edema for the treatment of edema associated with cardiac insufficiency and acute no-inflammatory tissue edema in dogs, cats and horses."

There is not a word about exercise-induced pulmonary hemorrhaging.

The Salix label cautions: "Federal law restricts this drug to use by or on the order of a licensed veterinarian."

In Kentucky, a Standardbred must be certified by a veterinarian to be treated with the medication, but a Thoroughbred trainer can treat his horse with it simply by requesting it, although it still must be administered by a vet.

Intervet calls Salix for dogs, cats and horses "an effective diuretic-saluretic which, if given in excessive amounts, may result in excessive dieresis which could result in electrolyte imbalance, dehydration and reduction of plasma volume enhancing the risk of circulatory collapse, thrombosis and embolism. Therefore, the animal should be observed for early signs of fluid depletion with electrolyte imbalance, and corrective measures administered."

Instead, racehorses are given the medication — which, as of mid-2002, was still being called Lasix by the *Daily Racing Form* and by most harness racing programs — and asked to perform strenuous exercise.

What does Lasix actually do inside a horse's body? In a paper published in 1977 in the *Journal of Equine Medicine and Surgery*, Drs. George Maylin, Tom Tobin, Richard Ray and Albert Gabel reviewed their findings:

"Injectible furosemide is a potent, effective, safe diuretic which, at the usual dose, has its peak diuretic effect in about 20 minutes in horses, at which time it increases urine output up to 40-fold for a short time. Most of its diuretic effect is within the first two hours after injection.

"During the first two hours, it decreased pressure in the right side of the heart, decreases left atrial pressure, decreases cardiac output, and, concurrently, it increases peripheral (systemic) blood vessel resistance and heart rate.

"It reduces edema in the lungs and airway of horses with certain respiratory diseases by one or more mechanisms, perhaps by lowering the pressure of the left atrium and/or increasing capacitance (ability to accept blood) of the vessels of the lung."

Most horsemen, as well as most veterinarians, consider Lasix a safe therapeutic medication — if not abused.

Whether or not massive, indiscriminate usage constitutes abuse is a difficult question.

If a horse's physical problems are being masked with the treatment of Lasix, is that abuse?

If horses who are dependent on medication are bred over and over again, is that abuse?

Few people in racing would deny that there are at least a few cheating horsemen who do use illegal drugs. If Lasix washes them out or masks their detection, is that abuse?

And what of racing's perception? If the general population, especially animal rights activists, realizes that virtually every Thoroughbred in California requires the diuretic Lasix and the analgesic Bute on race day, then what we perceive is not as important as what they perceive. That might be even worse than abuse for the racing industry. That could be suicide.

Chapter 4

Early Usage

The use of Lasix on horses was first documented in an article which appeared in the September, 1967 issue of *Veterinary Medicine/Small Animal Clinician.*

Titled "Furosemide in Equine Practices," the article was co-written by three veterinarians, Dr. Marvin G. Beeman, who went on to become president of the American Association of Equine Practitioners in 1975; Dr. Charles Vail, who also became president of the AAEP in 1985, and Dr. Harry Johnson of the Littleton Veterinary Clinic in Littleton, Colorado. The AAEP, headquartered in Lexington, Kentucky, was founded in 1954 as a non-profit organization. It currently has 6,500 members.

In the article, the three vets disclosed that they had been using a new drug, a furosemide called Lasix produced by the National Laboratory Corp., as an injectable diuretic in clinical trials for two years.

"I think furosemide was used in cattle for pneumonia first to help take away the edema in the lungs," Beeman said in March, 2002. "We just used it on bleeders to see if it would dry out a horse's lungs."

The three doctors found Lasix to be effective: "Results have been good in the treatment of localized edema associated with wounds, in snakebite, pre- and post-parturient edema, local congestive edema (i.e. 'stocking up'), laminitis, urticaria and idiopathic edema. In the muscular myopathy ('tying up') syndrome of horses, treatment has been successful when furosemide was used as conjunctive therapy."

About the effects of Lasix, the article noted, "There is a rapid onset of diuresis following administration of furosemide. This characteristic of the drug has been utilized to good advantage as a placebo and to produce micturtion for the collection of urine specimens."

The article then summarized three conditions "in which results with furosemide therapy have been consistently good." The three were laminitis, myositis or myopathy (tying up) and as a placebo.

There was no mention of exercise-induced pulmonary hemorrhaging.

Regardless, Beeman remains a staunch advocate of Lasix, even while he admits, "We still don't know why horses bleed." He does agree with just about everybody else as to the frequency of bleeding in horses: "Virtually every horse is going to bleed because of the hypertension of the pulmonary arteries which put pressure on the capillaries in the lungs."

In a March, 2002, interview, he offered his opinions about Lasix.

Regarding Lasix's effectiveness, he said, "It doesn't stop all horses from bleeding overtly, but it damn sure stops a lot of horses, not just race horses, from bleeding that way. Barrel racing, hunters, show horses. It damn well does. It works as well or better than any product. That's why people use it. It's not to enhance performance. The AAEP would have never used (endorsed) it if there was proof it helped horses beyond their capabilities. I was there when those rules were made. We felt that it was essential to the health and welfare of the horses."

Regarding a horse's weight loss when he uses Lasix, Beeman said, "At the dosage level given at the racetrack, I would have to see the data. I've heard discussions about it, but I don't know if I've seen any data for the doses given at the racetrack."

As to Lasix's ability to mask other drugs, he said, "People say it's a masking drug, and that's not true. It enhances the finding of a lot of drugs because it concentrates it in the urine."

Regarding the necessity of Lasix, he said, "Let me tell you something about that. If everyone would sign on for no race-day medication, I mean everybody, there would be no need for medication. There would be no need for chemists. That's as unrealistic as the sun not coming up in the East tomorrow morning. I would be for hay, oats and water if everybody would adhere to it. We expect these horses to run in the smog, run off an airplane and race all year long. To not give him medication is ludicrous."

About criticism of America's race-day medication from other countries, he said, "You have to be sure their testing is up to snuff. I don't buy the hypocrites of Europe who criticize us. I get tired of being told how bad we are in America. Why in hell don't they outrun us?"

As to banning the use of Lasix on two-year-olds, Beeman said, "If you're going to run two-year-olds, then why discriminate against them, the ones that bleed?"

Finally, regarding Lasix's ability to improve performance, documented by a critical study done in Pennsylvania and announced in 1990, he said, "If Lasix improves performance, if that was the case, then why the hell didn't the horses in the Pennsylvania study improve beyond their race times, which they did not? That's a very important point. The AAEP wouldn't have backed it if their times got better. That study proved that they ran to their abilities. Do you see any horses setting track records with Lasix? They improve because they'd been bleeding. Good handicappers pay attention to that."

Only if they know about it.

35

Chapter 5

Lasix in America

Andy Beyer, the esteemed author, columnist and handicapper from the *Washington Post/Daily Racing Form* — and originator of the Beyer Speed Figures used daily in the *Form* — wasn't sure what he was seeing at his home Maryland tracks in the 1970s when trainers there began using Lasix. "When it came around, I didn't know what it was," he said in a phone interview from the Gulfstream Park pressbox in March, 2002. "There was no name attached to it. The form in Maryland went absolutely haywire. Horses were just doing 20-length improvements overnight. You would see horses that would quit run all day long. One trainer would start working miracles. You'd see certain trainers, their barns would come alive."

This was, of course, long before simulcasting, so if horses at the Maryland tracks were suddenly running superbly for no apparent reason, the only ones who knew about it were Maryland horseplayers.

But no explanation was made to them. Medication information in the *Daily Racing Form* would not be included until 1990.

"None of this was made public," Beyer said. "I was writing, but when it first came in, I wasn't hip enough to know what it was. I was the new kid on the block. We didn't have that much awareness of drugs."

But Lasix's use on American racetracks may even have predated the 1970s. In his 1990 presentation to the American Association of Equine Practitioners, California veterinarian Dr. Rick Arthur wrote, "The history of the use of furosemide to treat bleeding is obscure. Harthill (Dr. Alex Harthill, a 77-year-old Kentucky veterinarian who was the president of the Kentucky Horsemen's Benevolent and Protective Association) is generally given credit for introducing furosemide to Thoroughbred racing in the late 1960s. Harthill does not take sole credit but admits to being one of the first to commonly use the drug." Arthur's source for that information was a personal communication with Harthill in July, 1990.

In March, 2002, when asked if he did, indeed, introduce Lasix to thoroughbred racing, Harthill said, "It started at the racetrack with me. I used it on Northern Dancer in 1964."

Four years later, Harthill was in the headlines as the attending veterinarian of Dancer's Image, who won the 1968 Kentucky Derby but tested positive for Butazolidin, an analgesic (painkiller) not allowed at the time. Dancer's Image was subsequently disqualified and Forward Pass declared the winner.

Writing in *Sports Illustrated*, Whitney Tower quoted Harthill giving a statement to *Louisville Courier-Journal* reporter Gail Evans, "No such drugs were administered by me."

That statement contradicted Harthill's own official statement a day earlier to Alvin Scham, director of security at Churchill Downs, when Harthill admitted giving Dancer's Image a shot of Bute the Saturday before the Derby, approximately 152 hours before the race.

Tower quoted Dr. Gene M. Bierhaus, a veterinarian for the Colorado Racing Commission for 17 years, saying the longest retention of Bute he was aware of was 78 hours.

The decision to disqualify Dancer's Image was hotly contested and appealed. The final appeal was dismissed in 1972, leaving Forward Pass as the winner of the 1968 Kentucky Derby.

It is worth noting that separate studies suggested that Bute may cause more damage than good. A study at Ohio State published in May, 2000, reported that Bute suppressed bone formation and healing. "The results are not that surprising, actually, that drugs which suppress inflammation might also slow healing," one of the researchers, Dr. Alicia Bertone said. "The take-home message is that Bute is not an innocuous drug, and horses that don't need it shouldn't be on it." Additionally, a study of Bute's side effects by Dr. Rebecca McConnico of Louisiana State University in 2002 said Bute has been associated with severe side effects including stomach ulcers, kidney dysfunction and inflammation/ulceration of the large colon. But that's material for another book.

In Maryland in the early 1970s, Beyer was too astute of a handicapper not to notice the sudden, incredible form reversals of some horses. "It was mostly a case of watching which trainer was working miracles," he said. "The first thing I noticed was that it tended to be more like speed horses were the ones who seemingly benefited. When we learned what it was about, the wake-up became consistent with horses who have respiratory problems."

In his book, *The Racing Imperative*, Dr. Joseph O'Dea, the past president of both the American Association of Equine Practitioners (in 1970) and the National Association of State Racing Commissioners (the predecessor of the Association of Racing Commissioners International), praised Beyer for bringing the questions about Lasix into the public: "Early on, the very observant racing writer and handicapper Andrew Beyer of the *Washington Post* observed the results of Lasix upon form and wrote about it often. He had his facts right for the most part, perceived the deleterious effects of Lasix upon handicapping and the destruction of formful racing. His writing brought industry-wide attention to the performance enhancing qualities of Lasix in some horses."

O'Dea's view of Lasix and race-day medication is about as opposite as possible to Dr. Marvin Beeman's. In his 1998 book, O'Dea, who was also a Thoroughbred owner and trainer, as well as a member of the New York State Racing and Wagering Board, wrote, "In its attempt to legitimize the use of performance altering Lasix, racing wrongfully used the bronchoscope to pathologize a normal response to a racing effort. The integrity of the contest upon which racing was built is destroyed when even one horse is allowed performance altering drugs. There would be no Lasix problem if Lasix did not enhance performance in some horses, or at least offer the prospect of enhancing performance."

It's a position he still believes in passionately. "People can't understand that we're not having true tests of races," he said in February, 2002. "There's no sport at all. I get so frustrated. It's the first rule of logic. You can't have a true race if a horse is on medication."

Beyer also has a jaundiced view of race-day medication. "When I was in Australia 10 years ago, there were no drugs," Beyer said in 2002. "These horses were like iron. If you look at the campaign of horses going into the Melbourne Cup, a horse would run a mile and a half prep three days before going two miles (the distance of the Melbourne Cup). Everyone else manages to get along without this stuff. The idea that we're the only country that can't survive without drugs is ridiculous. By creating a drug dependent breed, these horses, the American Thoroughbred, has regressed. The issue of the Triple Crown with the Belmont Stakes (until 1996, the Belmont Stakes was the only leg of the Triple Crown prohibiting race-day Lasix), was giving the sport a black eye. Somebody said, `The way to resolve this is to require all horses to run on Lasix and then it becomes a non-issue.' Essentially, that's what we've done."

Who knew what anybody was doing until 1990, when the *Daily Racing Form* began listing a horse's medication with its past performance lines?

Bettors were left to fend for themselves and guess which horses were racing not only on Lasix, but the analgesic Butazolidin (Bute) as well. Both began getting wide-spread use in the early

1970s, though many horsemen opposed one or both medications.

Paul Berube, now president and a member of the Board of Directors of the Thoroughbred Racing Protective Bureau, became the TRPB agent in Maryland in 1972 and heard about Lasix soon afterwards. "We began to hear about a drug that was turning horses around," he said. "It wasn't too long before Lasix was identified. When the Maryland Commission began to look at the drug from a regulatory standpoint, horsemen and vets quickly proclaimed it was needed for 'bleeders.' The hue and cry was so strong that the Commission approved its use with little or no controls. My distinct belief is that Lasix began as a 'cheating' drug that quickly morphed into therapeutic clothes. Of course, we now know Lasix does not prevent bleeding and, at most, may lessen bleeding in some horses. However, studies have shown it to be a performance enhancer. Although 1973 is the year of my first experience with Lasix, I have no doubt it was being used by a select few trainers and veterinarians prior to that. Eventually the word got out, and certainly, by 1973, Lasix was no longer a big secret on the track."

In a Sept. 12, 1973, *Daily Racing Form* story by Joe Hirsch, which noted that Colorado and California were the only two racing states allowing permissive medication at the time, trainer Budd Lepman, who raced in New Jersey and Florida, offered his opinion:

"I've changed my thinking about permissive medication. A number of years ago, when I was based in Chicago, I was very much in favor of the use of Butazolidin and other preparations designed to ease pain and alleviate inflammation. Over the years, I've had a chance to study the question and I'm strongly against racing on medication. Permissive medication leads to promiscuity."

On Dec. 4, 1974, New York trainer Frank "Pancho" Martin, on the way to his second of 10 consecutive training titles in New York, was suspended by the New York Racing Association stewards for 60 days after one of his horses tested positive for furosemide.

By 1975, Florida, Illinois, Kentucky, Louisiana, Maryland, Nebraska, New Mexico and Ohio had joined California and

Colorado in allowing medication.

In California, Lasix was being administered with little control. "The only rule concerning furosemide was that the California Horse Racing Board's Official Veterinarian had to be informed the next day on the daily report sheets," Dr. Rick Arthur said. "There were no rules governing time of administration, dosage or which horses received furosemide."

And no disclosure.

In a 1975 series in *American Turf Monthly* entitled "The ABC's of Drugs in Racing," then-senior editor Steve Davidowitz went after the states in that group of 10 that were not passing on medication information to the betting public: California, Colorado, Florida, Kentucky, Maryland and New Mexico. "Racing fans are not given drug information because the horsemen don't want them to have it," Davidowitz said. "And if the horsemen don't want them to have it, most state racing officials will go out of their way to find a reason to justify such a policy.

"Even beyond the need to eliminate suspicion from the public mind, the failure to release drug information may very well be unconstitutional. To deny one interested party — the betting fan — full access to pertinent information while other interested parties have that access is to provide some people — the horsemen — with an unfair competitive advantage. Horsemen are not barred from the betting windows, and many can and do take advantage of a system that gives them a tremendous built-in edge."

In writing about Davidowitz's series, Frank Phelps wrote in the Feb. 12, 1975, edition of the *Lexington Herald Leader* that Davidowitz cited a statistical study in Illinois, where medication information was public knowledge. The study didn't show an advantage for horses treated with Bute, "But the study did demonstrate a statistical edge for horses treated with Lasix," and is "apparently employed on horses not known to have bled previously. Moreover, the Lasix-treated winners paid prices 31 percent higher than winners that did not receive this drug."

New Jersey attacked the issue of Lasix in the mid-1970s. Lasix had been flowing freely at the state's racetracks until May, 1975, when the New Jersey Racing Commission banned its use except for certified bleeders. A bleeder could only be certified by the state veterinarian or the commission's two vets, who had to actually see the horse bleed either in a race or a workout.

The New Jersey Racing Commission held a hearing about Lasix at Monmouth Park, July 10, 1976. According to a story in the *Daily Racing Form* by George Bernet, the hearing could "best be described as a dead-heat" between pro and anti-Lasix factions.

Bernet wrote "Opposing factions lined up in traditional diverse order, with most horsemen and veterinarians favoring controlled medication to various degrees and stewards and track officials opposing it."

According to Bernet's story, Ron Gibson, a trainer representing the Horsemen's Benevolent and Protective Association, said that 84 percent of horsemen were in favor of controlled medication and cited the fact that horses were asked to race more in these days of year-round racing, and trainers and owners needed medication to get them through the ordeal in order to make expenses.

One of the speakers against the use of medication on race day was George Jaggard of Dalare Associates Testing Laboratory, the Commission's testing lab. According to Bernet's story, "Jaggard said that controlled medication causes problems because Lasix and Butazolidin can be given in either small or large doses and horses can be made to run hot or cold. He also said that when Lasix is used, testing becomes difficult and recommended a rule of no medication on the day of a race."

Jaggard offered a succinct commentary on race-day medication and its implications in an article he wrote in the Oct. 10, 1976, issue of the *British Journal of Sports Medicine*:

"The major problems of racing in the United States at the present time are caused by too much racing. This has led to too few

43

horses and small fields. Consequently many owners and trainers are trying to enter their horses too frequently and to race them when they are not really fit to run. The desire to race horses as frequently as possible has led to constant pressure from horsemen through their organizations for so called 'permissive medication.'

"Started in the state of Colorado approximately ten years ago, this has grown until finally there are only a few states, notably New York and New Jersey, that have resisted the pressure.

"The drug that gave the opening wedge to permissive medication was phenylbutazone, but this in many states has led to the inclusion of other drugs, including analgesics and drugs that veterinarians claim are needed for therapeutic purposes. Some states have endeavored to control phenylbutazone medication by quantitation and while lower limits cause little difficulty, maximum allowable limits have caused problems and are not practical. While there has been no publicity to my knowledge about frusemide (furosemide, Lasix), the abuse of this drug for so called 'bleeders' is an example that may seriously interfere with drug detection in urine and its use should be confined to proven 'bleeders' (i.e., horses suffering from epistaxis).

"Pre-race blood testing began roughly ten years ago at the harness tracks and has been resisted by our flat tracks rather successfully up to the present time. The blood testing methods and those used by the same laboratories in post-race urine testing is inadequate and will not detect many illegal drugs."

But one didn't have to be burrowing through obscure medical journals to get the point. It was hammered out quite nicely by Eclipse Award-winning columnist Maryjean Wall, who wrote about the Lasix battle in New Jersey in the *Lexington Herald Leader*, Dec. 15, 1977.

Under the headline "Unlimited Use of Lasix Could Become a Monster," she wrote:

"Well known among even the amateur needle artists is the ability of Lasix to interfere with drug testing by reducing urinary concentrations of certain medications such as Bute, some painkillers and some tranquilizers."

Wall's column was full of interesting items, noting that in Kentucky, harness horses were not permitted to race under any medication while Thoroughbreds could.

She quoted Dr. Arthur Davidson, a Kentucky racetrack veterinarian, describing how far trainers would go to get their horses certified as bleeders so they could receive Lasix: "The trainers got so desperate that they'd draw blood out of their ponies and shoot it up into their horses' noses so that the veterinarian, when he arrived, would think the horse had been bleeding."

Wall wrote, "As has happened too many times where medication is permissive more than it is controlled, the ones to lose are those who support the game, the horseplayers who never know what's really going on."

Apparently, a lot of people didn't know what was really going on. Prior to Wall's column, on July 8, 1977, a story by Bud Burns in the *Daily Racing Form* said the New Jersey Racing Commission "appeared surprised" to learn from the company which manufactured Lasix that it had been approved by the U.S. Food and Drug Administration for the treatment of edema and had never been approved to treat horses who bleed.

The news was related to the Commission by Dr. Roger Conant, a veterinarian in clinical research with The National Laboratory Corp., of Somerville, N.J., a subsidiary of Hoechst Roussel. Conant stated that Lasix's ability to treat bleeders "might have started from an accidental discovery by a veterinarian treating a horse with edema who also was a bleeder."

According to the story in the *Form*, Racing Commissioner Chairman Charles Catella, then asked Conant why shouldn't the public know about this limited FDA approval. Conant replied, "We're making this known to the public today."

Conant also said that his company hadn't been able to set up a study to test the effects of Lasix on horses who bleed. "We can't recommend a product if we can't substantiate its effectiveness," he said.

That's not all Conant said. According to the story in the *Form*, "Conant said his firm's test did show that Lasix might help to conceal the presence of Butazolidin in a urine test, but not in a blood test. 'Blood tests might be in order,' he said."

That suggestion came right from the manufacturer of Lasix.

Twenty-five years later, the state of New Hampshire was still testing urine samples only.

And Lasix is more popular than ever.

Chapter 6

Other Points of View

Dr. Thomas Tobin of the Kentucky Equine Drug Testing Program at the University of Kentucky, was one of the first researchers to publish a study about Lasix. He said Lasix was already being used when he arrived in Kentucky in 1975.

In studies he co-authored in 1976[1] and 1978[2], Tobin documented that:

• Blood tests must be used to detect Bute if Lasix is also administered to a horse.

• Concentrations of furosemide in urine are up to a thousand-fold greater than in plasma.

• Lasix is rapidly eliminated from the bloodstream of the horse.

• Very high concentrations of Lasix are found in urine long after it can no longer be detected in plasma.

Tobin went to bat for Lasix in *Drugs and The Performance Horse*, published by Charles C. Thomas of Springfield, Illinois, noting in capital letters:

LASIX DOES NOT FLUSH DRUGS OUT OF THE BLOODSTREAM OF HORSES, PERIOD.

---

[1] Roberts, Brian L., J.W. Blake and Thomas Tobin, "Drug Interactions in the Horse: Effect of Furosemide on Plasma and Urinary Levels of Phenylbutazone," Research Communications in Chemical Pathology and Pharmacology, Vol. 15, No. 2, October, 1976
[2] Roberts, Brian L., J.W. Blake and Thomas Tobin, "The Pharmacology of Furosemide in the Horse. Its Detection, Pharmacokinetics, and Clearance From Urine," April, 1978

Tobin then cited a study done by Carl Larsen of the Standardbred Commission in Kentucky on 58 Standardbreds who were put on Lasix, then the only permitted medication at Louisville Downs, in the summer of 1977. There were 160 clockings of the 58 horses before they were put on Lasix and 232 after Lasix was added. The figures showed, Tobin said, that horses placed on Lasix were 0.14 seconds slower.

Tobin wrote, "The only conclusion from this study seems to be that the horsemen in Louisville Downs in the summer of 1977 were not, on the whole, able to improve the performance of their horses with furosemide, and it would seem reasonable to extend this experimental result to other horses and horsemen. Lengthy speculation such as one hears, and occasionally sees published, about possible mechanisms by which furosemide improves the performance of horses are therefore not valid."

Why the state of Kentucky, so proud of its Thoroughbred heritage, would base its policy on Lasix on a single study of Standardbreds at Louisville Downs is not addressed. What's most interesting is that, as of 2002, a Standardbred trainer must present a bleeder certificate to race his horse on Lasix, while a Thoroughbred trainer need only ask for it. Also, Standardbreds in Kentucky are allowed a maximum Lasix dose of 5 cc. (250 milligrams), but Thoroughbreds in Kentucky have no maximum dose.

Tobin concluded, "Lasix has been widely and also very incorrectly reported to 'flush' drugs out of horses. Lasix does not flush drugs out of horses. 'Masking' of drugs by Lasix is a problem that has not been studied or reported on and does not appear to be significant. The conclusion that Lasix does not improve the performance of horses under racing conditions seems at this time to be inescapable."

In 1978, the National Association of State Racing Commissioners, the predecessor of the Association of Racing Commissioners International, convened a Blue Ribbon panel to review both Lasix and Bute. A year later, the NASRC Veterinarians-Chemists Subcommittee recommended that the NASRC allow Lasix in its non-binding medication guidelines. Instead, the NASRC banned Lasix in 1981, and 24 racing jurisdictions followed its lead. The reason? The threat of direct federal intervention in drug testing of racehorses.

On May 16, the Corrupt Horse Racing Practices Act of 1980 was introduced in Congress. That bill would prohibit all medication 24 hours prior to post; create a pre-race testing facility; set minimum laboratory standards at every racetrack; provide harsh penalties, including prison sentences, for any trainer and owner whose horse tested positive, and bring racing under the regulatory jurisdiction of the Drug Enforcement Administration, an arm of the Justice Department.

How do you think that sat with state racing commissions around the country? One racing jurisdiction after another re-examined its Lasix and Bute policies.

"The recent changes in medication policies are an attempt to defuse the bill," Steve Crist wrote in a Sept. 10, 1980, story in the *New York Times*. In that story, Crist quoted Charles Schmidt, chairman of the Illinois Racing Commission and of the NASRC Medication Panel, about the prospect of federal supervision of drug testing: "The legislation would be disastrous, and I oppose it completely. But I have to agree 100 percent with those who say that we in the racing business asked for it."

Actually, as Crist documented in his story, the impetus for drug reform came from Illinois, where Donna Ewing, a housewife who had founded the Illinois Hooved Animal Humane Society five years earlier, attended a public hearing called in 1976 by the Illinois Racing Commission. The Commission wanted to increase its permissible dosage levels on Bute.

Ewing did not speak, but instead met with Robert Baker, a horse owner who had become concerned over the use of drugs. With the help of Ewing's organization, Baker spent 18 months studying the issue to prepare "The Misuse of Drugs in Horse Racing," which, Crist said in his story, "shook the racing industry."

Just a month before Baker's report was published, a tragic accident at Pimlico Race Course in Baltimore focused national attention on Bute. Robert Pineda, a 25-year-old jockey, was killed when his mount, Easy Edith, broke down in the stretch. Easy Edith had been racing on Bute, and two other jockeys who were injured in the race, Johnny Adams and Rudy Turcotte, said that Easy Edith would have felt the pain of a broken leg and pulled herself up had she not been racing on Bute.

Crist called Baker's report "laboriously documented." Among Baker's findings were that pre-race use of Bute was physiologically destructive to horses because it forced them to run on injuries which had not healed; that pre-race medication had led to smaller fields and fewer starts per horse, and that Lasix was frequently used to increase urine production and flush out the evidence of more potent and illegal drugs.

In following months, "talk began to surface that some trainers were using Lasix to mask a narcotic marketed as Sublimaze and known on the backstretch as 'rocket fuel,'" Crist wrote.

When a test for Sublimaze was developed, many positives ensued, providing even more momentum for a new stance on race-day medication.

In April, 1980, the NASRC concluded a one-year study with medication guidelines embraced by all but three racing states, Delaware, West Virginia and Kentucky.

Crist wrote, "Those three are the last bastions of pro-medication forces. The reasons for resistance in each reflect trainers' and owners' objections to ending the medication programs. Delaware says that, with only 50 racing dates a year, it cannot afford to enforce the guidelines; West Virginia horsemen, such as the trainer Dale Baird, the perennial national leader in races won, say that the sudden rule changes would immobilize their stable operations; Kentucky says it knows better than anyone else what is good for a horse."

A year later, on April 8, 1981, the NASRC banned Lasix, 24-0, with three abstentions and one absence.

Voting to ban Lasix were: Arizona, Arkansas, California, Florida, Idaho, Illinois, Kentucky (Thoroughbred), Kentucky (harness), Massachusetts, Michigan, Montana, Nebraska, Nevada, New Mexico, New York, Ohio, Oregon, Pennsylvania (harness), Puerto Rico, South Dakota, Vermont, Washington, West Virginia and Wyoming. Colorado, Louisiana and Pennsylvania Thoroughbred abstained. New Jersey was not present. The Canadian provinces were not polled because Canada had already banned Lasix, though it would later allow it.

The Lasix ban did not sit well with horsemen, who successfully lobbied for its return. By 1983, Lasix was being allowed in California, Colorado, Florida, Kentucky for both Thoroughbred and harness, Louisiana, Maryland for Thoroughbred only, Michigan, Nebraska, New Jersey, Pennsylvania for Thoroughbred only and West Virginia.

By 1985, only three major Thoroughbred racing states, Arizona, Arkansas and New York, did not allow Lasix.

Lasix's return to popularity centered on an alleged solution to the problem of Lasix interfering with drug testing: guidelines for dose, time and method of administration, guidelines which are still being ignored by several racing jurisdictions 20 years later.

Those guidelines are for a dose of 150 to 250 milligrams (three to five cc.), administered no less than four hours before post time, intravenously.

That "magic" formula, which allegedly would ensure that Lasix did not interfere with detection of other drugs, was proposed by the American Association of Equine Practitioners (AAEP).

Curiously, the NASRC, which morphed into the Association of Racing Commissioners International, did not adopt that "Model Rule for Furosemide" until May, 1996.

Arriving at those numbers was an arduous journey. "In the

period 25 years ago, when we first began making noise about urine testing, we were getting samples from racetracks where the urine looked like water," Dr. Rick Sams of Ohio State University said. "It didn't look like urine at all. The reason was because those samples had been taken from horses that had just been given Lasix. The administration of Lasix close to race time interfered with our ability to test urine. We first talked about it in 1978."

In a presentation at "Furosemide in the Horse; Its Actions, Effects and Regulatory Control," a Testing Integrity Program Seminar held in New Orleans on March 1, 1998, Sams summarized the research which led to the "magic" formula:

"In the late 1970s, a study by a group of analysts representing seven laboratories in the United States looked at 12 drugs from various chemical and pharmacological classes (apomorphine, fentanyl, pentazocine, nalbuphine, butorphanol, oxymorphone, acepromazine, methylphenidate, piperacepazine, alaphrodine, amitrippyline and methamphetamine) administered to horses by various routes. Furosemide was administered at doses of 0.5 to 1.0 milligram per kilogram intravenously at various times before and after these drugs were administered. Urine samples were collected from the horses at various times after drug administration, divided and sent to the seven racing laboratories.

"The seven laboratories tested for all of these drugs by thin layer chromatographic methods with the exception of fenatyl. The laboratories reported back to Dr. (George) Maylin (of Cornell University) and myself that the administration of furosemide resulted in some degree of interference in the detection of all these substances except pentazocine and methamphetamine for as long as six hours after furosemide administration."

That should have ended any debate about Lasix's ability to mask other drugs. That should have been more than enough evidence to ban race-day use of Lasix. And it may have contributed to the NASRC ban in 1981.

But horsemen were not about to live with that ban. "This

action by the NASRC prompted a series of meetings in which the Horsemen's Benevolent and Protective Association pressed for some relief from the prohibition of furosemide," Sams said. "The American Horse Council assembled a task force on medication and convened a series of meetings to discuss medication issues. They also proposed legislation that would regulate the use of drugs in racehorses.

"A particularly important breakthrough came when the AAEP (American Association of Equine Practitioners) reported their recommendation with regard to the dose, time and route of administration of furosemide."

The recommendation prompted the American Horse Council to ask the analysts to repeat the study of furosemide's interference with drug detection using a dose of 250 milligrams (5 cc.) administered intravenously four hours before collection of urine samples.

Testing was done at Sams' Ohio State University facility and Maylin's lab at Cornell University. "It was concluded that furosemide did not interfere with the detection of any of these drugs if the dose of furosemide was 250 mg and the route of administration was IV," Sams said.

So, how, exactly, in the year 2002, can horses receive double that dose of Lasix in Florida, New Jersey, New York, Washington and West Virginia? Why do other states, including Kentucky for Thoroughbreds, not even list a dose, or a time of administration or a method of administration? Colorado and Michigan explicitly allow Lasix to be administered intramuscularly, a method which has been documented to lengthen the effects of Lasix.

Asked about his opinion of Lasix in 2002, Tobin said, "The principal thing that has changed was that we thought it didn't influence performance. It is considered it does because of the weight change. Other than that, I don't think anything has changed at all in terms of the largest context. After the '70s and early '80s, we figured out how it affects drug detection, and racing put in the four-hour rule."

Something had to be done. The late Illinois Congressman Robert McClory, speaking about the Corrupt Horse Racing Practice Act Bill before the United States House of Representatives Judiciary Subcommittee on Criminal Justice, said, "The United States is the only country that permits the practices of drugging and numbing race horses. Although various racing states have legalized what is termed controlled medication, it is anything but that. Horse racing is becoming drug dependent. Many of the drugs used are illegal and untested. And all are inadequately controlled at the state level. While they push for increased revenues from racing, prolonged seasons and lenient drug policies, state legislatures are ignoring the horse as a living creature. The artificial means to enhance a horse's moneymaking capacity defeat integrity."

On May 18, 1983, Tobin testified about Lasix, Bute and drug testing before the same United States House of Representatives Judiciary Subcommittee on Criminal Justice.

Among the highlights of Tobin's testimony was a statement which seemed to bear little resemblance to the results of the first test study of Lasix coordinated by Sams and Maylin which showed that Lasix did interfere with drug testing for a multitude of drugs for as long as six hours: "It (furosemide) does not reduce the level of any drug in the body of a horse."

Tobin also testified, "By giving Lasix four hours prior to post time, at the anti-epistaxis dose (250 mg IV), no masking or drug dilution effects or interference with drug testing is encountered. Denial of horsemen the right to use this drug in racing horses is illogical in terms of human endeavor and inhumane to the horses."

Testifying about Bute, Tobin said, "It is thought to enable a horse to perform to his innate ability and it enables horsemen to field racing sound horses. Use of this type of medication is entirely legal, ethical and humane in human sports medicine. There is absolutely no reason to think that it is otherwise in veterinary medicine."

Maybe Tobin should have consulted with jockey Robert Pineda's family first or the other jockeys injured when Pineda's mount went down at Pimlico and Pineda lost his life. Writing about phenylbutazone, Dr. Kenneth Hinchcliff of Ohio State University's College of Veterinary Medicine said, "The pain associated with suspensory desmitis (inflammation of the soft tissues in the suspensory) is readily controlled by phenylbutazone, but allowing a horse with suspensory desmitis (who was) treated with phenylbutazone to race likely increases the risk of a catastrophic breakdown injury and risk to other horses in the field and jockeys."

There were other voices heard in 1983 in two high-profile stories which ran three days apart.

On June 6, 1983, Crist, now the Chairman and Publisher of the *Daily Racing Form*, wrote a story for the *New York Times* about Lasix that was picked up by the *Lexington Herald Leader* and other newspapers nationally through the *New York Times* News Service. The headline of Crist's story in the *Lexington Herald* was:

The Mystery Drug:
Controversy Rages
Over Use of Lasix

In his story, Crist quoted Jerry Fanning, the trainer of Desert Wine, who finished second in the Kentucky Derby and the Preakness, racing on Lasix in both: "Lasix can turn a $10,000 horse into a $50,000 horse and a slow one into a fast one."

Desert Wine's trainer and owners had gone to court to allow Desert Wine to be treated with Lasix in the Preakness. The Maryland Thoroughbred Board altered its rules to allow Desert Wine to be placed on the bleeder list on an internal exam. Board Chairman Robert Banning said at the time, "You'll have 99 percent of the horses running on Lasix now."

Cornell University's Dr. George Maylin, then head of the Drug Testing Quality Assistance Program of the National Association of State Racing Commissioners, told Crist, "All the research shows that Lasix definitely improves performance. We don't know why, but it does a lot more than what it's used for."

Nineteen years have done little to alter Maylin's understanding of Lasix or of his opinion about it. "Very candidly, we don't know much more now than we did in the early '70s when it became the rage," Maylin said in 2002. "I don't think there's been any documented stories showing that it stops bleeding. At most, it minimizes the bleeding. I don't think there's any pseudo-science showing that says it stops bleeding. That is a misconception."

Maylin is convinced Lasix does a lot more: "There's a reason trainers are using Lasix, and it isn't bleeding. I think it's to help performance. I think it's generally accepted by horsemen that it helps horses. The mechanism is unknown. They use bleeding as a cover."

Maylin also believes Lasix can mask other drugs. "If it's not controlled, absolutely. The advocates will say Lasix doesn't interfere with drug testing if it's regulated. The reality is that very few states regulate in a way that it doesn't. New York and Maryland do."

Crist wrote, "Horsemen and sophisticated bettors have been on to Lasix for some time: Horses on Lasix run over their heads. One of the most powerful betting angles at Thoroughbred tracks in some states is betting a horse who is running on Lasix for the first time. Information about which horses use Lasix is available on the track programs in New Jersey, as it is in Maryland and Florida among other states. In California and Kentucky, however, fans have no idea which horses are receiving the drug."

Crist presented another viewpoint on Lasix, that of trainer D. Wayne Lukas, who told Crist, "I use Lasix on fewer of my horses than a lot of California trainers. But it's a humane drug that only makes horses better and lets them race longer. I would think that people in the industry would applaud a drug that makes our horses happier and able to perform better and for longer periods of time."

Just two days later, horse racing received more national coverage: A cover story in *USA Today*.

The headline to Chet Czarniak's story was:

Controversy:
Drugs and Racehorses

A sub-head said:

Veterinarians to meet next week;
new guidelines may follow

If that wasn't provocative enough, there was a huge table showing which states allowed bute and Lasix, featuring a graphic of a pair of hands filling up a syringe from a bottle set against the background of several horses competing in a race.

Citing the American Horse Council as its source, *USA Today* reported that of the 28 states conducting horse racing in the United States, California, Colorado, Florida, Kentucky, Louisiana, Maryland (for Thoroughbreds only, not Standardbreds), Michigan, Nebraska, New Jersey, Pennsylvania (for Thoroughbreds only, not Standardbreds) and West Virginia allowed Lasix as of May 15, 1983. Arizona, Arkansas, Delaware, Idaho, Illinois, Maine, Massachusetts, Montana, New Hampshire, New Mexico, New York, Ohio, Oregon, South Dakota, Vermont, Washington and Wyoming did not.

In his story, Czarniak pointed out that when the Florida Department of Business Regulation banned Lasix, horsemen staged a two-day boycott at Calder Race Course and got the state legislature to re-authorize its use.

Weighing both sides, Czarniak noted that several animal

protection agencies maintained that Lasix has no value in reducing bleeding in racehorses and that its urine-increasing properties made it tougher to detect illegal drugs.

Czarniak cited a 1981 study done at the University of Pennsylvania that showed that Lasix had "some apparent success" in reducing bleeding, but also that the study concluded Lasix was not effective in all horses and that 56 percent of the 85 horses studied still bled after using Lasix.

Czarniak then wrote, "Lasix, however, does not seem to be a drug that artificially stimulates a horse, making it run better. One study of horses during swimming exercises showed no significant change in heart or blood rate between those using Lasix and those not.

"Scientists recently also found the charge that Lasix dilutes other drugs — veterinarians are careful to say it does not mask or hide other drugs — need not be a concern."

Fast forward 19 years. We still do not know exactly what Lasix does. But we do know this. Getting a cover story in *USA Today* was a great coup for horse racing — if there hadn't been an accompanying graphic of someone filling up a syringe.

Chapter 7

Does It Work? 1980s Version

Not everyone in the early 1980s had Dr. Tom Tobin's zeal for Lasix. Other scientists even questioned if it worked.

In three separate studies from 1981 through 1984, Lasix's ability to treat exercise induced pulmonary hemorrhaging (EIPH) was challenged, and the results suggested Lasix was far from a panacea for bleeders.

In the May, 1981, issue of the *American Journal of Veterinary Research*, a study co-authored by Dr. John Pascoe and Dr. Rick Arthur[1] assessed EIPH in Thoroughbreds. They investigated 235 Thoroughbreds with a fiberoptic endoscope within two hours of racing to determine the frequency of EIPH. One hundred and three of the 235 (43.8 percent) had various degrees of hemorrhage in the tracheal lumen (inside of the trachea) which appeared to originate from the lung. Two of the 103 bled through the nostrils (0.8 percent). Though a greater percentage of five-year-olds and older horses had EIPH, the study concluded there was no relationship between EIPH and a horse's age, sex, or finish in the race.

Fifty-six of the horses with EIPH were treated with Lasix. Thirty of the 56 still had evidence of pulmonary hemorrhage. Nineteen of the 30 had visible functional abnormalities of the upper

---

[1] Pascoe, J.R., G.L. Ferraro, J.H. Cannon, R.M. Arthur and J.D. Wheat, "Exercise-Induced Pulmonary Hemorrhage in Racing Thoroughbreds: A Preliminary Study," *American Journal of Veterinary Research*, May, 1981

respiratory tract, forcing the researchers to conclude, "The efficacy of furosemide for the treatment of EIPH was questioned."

In the July, 1984, issue of *The Cornell Veterinarian*, a study done at the New Bolton Center School of Veterinary Medicine at the University of Pennsylvania by doctors Corinne Sweeney, Lawrence Soma, Cynthia Bucan and Susan Ray explored furosemide's ability to stop EIPH-related bleeding against other medications.[2]

The researchers chose three Thoroughbreds with a "confirmed history" of EIPH and treated each one before exercise with four different medications: atropine sulfate, a pre-anesthetic used to minimize salvation; cromolyn, a mast cell stabilizer used for allergy-caused asthma; ipratropium, a bronchodilator, and furosemide.

The study's introduction noted EIPH's prevalence in not only Thoroughbreds, but also in horses in various competitive events such as three-day events and polo matches. "Therapeutic approaches to EIPH have either been empirical or based on unproven hypotheses," the study said. "The efficacy of available medication has been anecdotal and unsupported by clinical trials. The present study was designed to determine the efficacy of atropine, cromolyn, ipratropium and furosemide in the prevention of EIPH in Thoroughbreds."

The researchers examined the three Thoroughbreds with known histories of EIPH. One was leased to the University of Pennsylvania specifically for the study; one was racing and purchased by the authors for use in the study, and the third was donated to the university.

All horses were in "excellent health and remained so throughout the duration of the study."

The horses were exercised under saddle to induce EIPH. A

[2] Sweeney, C.R., L.R. Soma, C.A. Bucan and S.G. Ray, "Exercise-Induced Pulmonary Hemorrhage in Exercising Thoroughbreds: Preliminary Results With Pre-Exercise Medication," *The Cornell Veterinarian*, July, 1984

training period of three weeks was needed before adequate speeds could be reached to produce EIPH. A standard distance and speed was established for each horse which would cause that horse to be positive 100 percent of the time when examined with an endoscope one hour following exercise. The horses were exercised daily and fed hay and mixed grain.

A minimum of five consecutive weekly control runs were conducted to establish that the horse was positive for EIPH at the chosen speed and distance. After that, one or two controlled runs were conducted following every three drug trials. The minimum time interval between the runs, either control runs or drug trials, was five days. None of the horses ever showed clinical signs of respiratory difficulty before or after the runs.

Here are the results:

The administration of 15 milligrams of atropine IV one hour before exercise prevented EIPH in Horse A on all three trials, in Horse B one of six trials and in Horse C zero of six trials for a total of four of 15 trials.

Twenty cc. of a two percent solution of cromolyn was administered by nebulization into a nasotracheal tube passed into the pharynx. Cromolyn prevented EIPH in one of four trials for Horse A and zero of four trials for both Horses B and C for a total of one of 15 trials.

Ten cc. of a one percent solution of ipratropium administered in the same method as cromolyn prevented EIPH in all eight trials by Horse B and seven of eight by Horse C for a total of 15 of 16 trials. (Horse A was returned to his former owner before trials were done on him with cromolyn.)

Furosemide was administered at various doses and times before exercise, including a dose of 350 milligrams intravenously four hours before exercising, 350 milligrams intravenously two hours prior to exercise, 600 milligrams intravenously four hours prior to exercising, and a combination of 250 milligrams intramuscularly five hours prior to exercise and 250 milligrams intravenously one hour prior to exercise. Water was withheld from the horses from the time of furosemide administration until completion of the exercise.

Furosemide was used in four trials by all three horses. EIPH continued every single time for a total of zero for 12.

Regarding the obvious low number of horses in the experiment, the study said, "The number of horses in this study was small, but was due to the expense of maintaining Thoroughbred racehorses in training for months. However, this small group gave the authors an opportunity to do multiple trials with a number of drugs with varying pharmacological activities as means of establishing possible physiological mechanisms.

One of the study's conclusions was that horses began bleeding again after reaching a "breezing form. This confirms the general observation that a period of rest does not stop EIPH in horses."

Regarding the great success of ipratropium in stopping EIPH, the study said, "The pharmacological properties of ipratropium in the horse have not been studied, but based on human investigation, it seems most probable that the bronchodilator effects are responsible for preventing EIPH in the two horses."

And furosemide? "The efficacy of furosemide in the prevention of exercise-induced pulmonary hemorrhage has never been documented," the study said.

Soma and Sweeney did another 1984 study[3] comparing the EIPH-stopping capability of furosemide vs. hesperidin-citrus bioflavinoids. In a larger sample of 85 Thoroughbreds with a history of EIPH, 61 were administered furosemide four hours prior to racing. Thirty-four of the 61 continued to bleed (55.7 percent). Of the 24 Thoroughbreds not treated with furosemide, 17 (70.8 percent) bled afterwards. The other drug stopped bleeding in only

---

[3] Sweeney, C.R., and L.R. Soma, "Exercise-Induced Pulmonary Hemorrhage in Thoroughbred Horses: Response to Furosemide or Hesperidin-Citrus Bioflavinoids," *Journal of the American Veterinary Medical Association*, July, 1984

seven of 45 Thoroughbreds tested. Regarding furosemide, the study concluded, "There was no statistically significant difference between the treated and the non-treated groups."

Lasix, though, did diminish bleeding in a 1985 study done by Pascoe and Rick Arthur. The study examined 44 Thoroughbreds after workouts a minimum of four times, twice when they were not treated, once after they were treated with saline and once when they were treated with furosemide. The study concluded, "Although furosemide did not stop EIPH, it did reduce the EIPH score in 28 horses (63.7 percent)."

Lasix's inability to stop bleeding was inescapable. It diminished bleeding in some horses. What else did it do?

Soma co-authored another Lasix study in 1985 with Drs. L. Laster, F. Oppenlander and V. Barr-Alderfer.[4]

One hundred and twenty-eight Thoroughbreds were selected for the study from Keystone (now Philadelphia Park) and four racetracks in Maryland: Bowie, Laurel, Pimlico and Timonium. The Thoroughbreds with EIPH were divided into three groups and were monitored for 10 races, five before being administered furosemide and five afterwards.

• Group 1 consisted of Thoroughbreds who bled at the nostrils within one hour after a race or workout.

• Group 2 consisted of Thoroughbreds whose bleeding was only detected by endoscopic examination.

• Group 3 consisted of Thoroughbreds who bled at the nostrils during a race or immediately after a race.

Furosemide was administered four hours before race time in a detention barn.

A fourth group (control group) of randomly selected Thoroughbreds was not treated with furosemide.

Each group was split into estimated value categories of

---

[4] Soma, L.R., L. Laster, F. Oppenlander and V. Barr-Alderfer, "Effects of Furosemide on the Racing Times of Horses With Exercise-Induced Pulmonary Hemorrhage," *American Journal of Veterinary Research*, Vol. 46, No. 4, April, 1985

lower than $10,000 or greater than $10,000. Thus there were six groups of horses treated with furosemide. Five of the six groups showed faster times after being administered Lasix, the lone exception being the Group 1 horses valued at under $10,000, whose times increased slightly. Times of the control group had greater increases.

Horses with EIPH who had not bled at the nostrils and were treated with furosemide raced faster. The study concluded that furosemide had a more pronounced effect on higher-value, higher-speed horses; that furosemide did not have an effect in all horses, and that EIPH did not affect all horses uniformly.

A 1988 study confirmed the obvious about Lasix: its administration decreased a horse's weight significantly.[5] The study disclosed that six horses treated with furosemide weighed 19.2 kilograms (42.3 pounds) less — the equivalent of four percent of his body weight — eight hours later, compared to a control group of five horses who were not treated, but kept in the exact same environment and weighed 8 kilograms (19.3 pounds) less eight hours later. The difference was 23 pounds.

Think about what that means in the performance of a Thoroughbred. If an apprentice jockey with a five-pound weight allowance is half-good, dozens of trainers will use him to get five pounds of weight off their Thoroughbred. How could losing more than 20 pounds not help a horse perform better?

---

[5] Freestone, J.F., G.P. Carlson, D.R. Harrold and G. Church, "Influence of Furosemide Treatment on Fluid and Electrolyte Balance in Horses," *American Journal of Veterinary Research*, November, 1988

Chapter 8

The Cup and The Crown

As the medication debate over Lasix raged on in the '80s, Thoroughbred racing and harness racing launched an unprecedented series of championship races in the same year: 1984.

The Thoroughbred industry chose to stage its championship races on a single afternoon at one track.

Called the Breeders' Cup, it debuted at Hollywood Park and was an instant smash. NBC's four-hour live television coverage and the furious three-horse stretch battle between longshot winner Wild Again, Slew o' Gold and Gate Dancer in the inaugural Breeders' Cup Classic gave the afternoon of championship races instant credibility.

The *Daily Racing Form* did not publish each horse's medication with its past performance lines until July 1, 1990. Thus the first year the "L" for Lasix appeared in Breeders' Cup races was 1991, when 40 of 90 horses in the seven championship races used furosemide, 44.4 percent.

By 1996, it was 65.9 percent. The following year, it jumped to 88.2 percent.

In the 2000 Breeders' Cup at Churchill Downs, 91.3 percent of the horses raced on Lasix. In 2001 at Belmont Park, 90 of 94 horses used Lasix, 95.7 percent.

The only horses not on Lasix in the 2001 Breeders' Cup at Belmont were Neil Drysdale-trained Bella Belluci, who was third in the Juvenile Filly, and three horses trained by France's Andre

65

Fabre, the winner and third-place finishers in the Filly & Mare Turf, Banks Hill (GB) and Spring Oak (GB), and Slew The Red, who was ninth in the Turf.

"Bella Belluci had never been treated with Lasix," Drysdale said in March, 2002. "She had never shown any indication of bleeding."

But in her next start, her three-year-old debut in the Santa Paula Stakes at Santa Anita, March 24, 2002, Bella Belluci ran with Lasix and Bute, winning by half a length at odds of 4-5. She raced on Lasix again in her next start, when she romped in the Comely Stakes at Aqueduct April 14.

Fabre, asked why he didn't use Lasix on his three Breeders' Cup starters in an April 12, 2002, phone interview, said, "Because they didn't bleed. They were running well. For me, most horses bleed when they're not properly trained. They don't have a foundation, or enough rest between races. You can bleed them (make them bleed), if you work them when they're coughing or have an inflammation."

Long since recognized as one of the world's greatest conditioners, Fabre has been the leading trainer in France every year since 1987. His victories include a record five Prix de l'Arc de Triomphes in his native country; three consecutive Coronation Cups, the 2000 Guineas, English Oaks and St. Leger Stakes in England; the Irish Derby and Irish Oaks in Ireland; and three Breeders' Cup races, the 1990 Turf with In The Wings, the 1993 Classic with 133-1 longshot Arcangues and the 2001 Filly & Mare Turf with Banks Hill.

Fabre has 140 horses in his stable and does not favor the use of Lasix. "It's not a scientific point of view, but I don't think it improves horses," he said. "For me, that is all rubbish. Who proved this? It's just the vets. I used to be a jockey. I took Lasix to lose weight. You piss for two hours and pass the weight, but you're dead. I was no good on my horse. I'm convinced some trainers get their horses to bleed to get Lasix. For me, it is psychological help for the trainers and owners, instead of the horses. It would be better to find another way to train horses so they don't bleed."

A European trainer who used Lasix in the 2001 Breeders' Cup was John Gosden from England, whose Crystal Music finished seventh in the 12-horse Filly & Mare Turf. "She had shown signs (of bleeding) on the endoscopic examination," Gosden said in a February, 2002, phone interview. "I had to get a certificate from the vet here in England."

From 1999 through 2001, 278 of 299 Breeders' Cup starters used Lasix, 93.0 percent.

From 1999 through 2001, all 40 starters in the Breeders' Cup Classic raced on Lasix. Since 1997, only one horse started in the Breeders' Cup Classic without Lasix, Arch, who finished ninth of 10 in 1998. How smart do you have to be to see something wrong when 58 of 59 starters in the most important and richest North American race of the year, the Breeders' Cup Classic, raced on Lasix the past five years?

This is nothing short of disgraceful.

Are we to believe that in the space of 10 years there was an outbreak of bleeding that justified a jump from 44.4 percent to 95.7 percent?

Of course there wasn't.

When are people going to stop looking the other way?

When are Thoroughbred racing officials going to summon the courage to say, "We should not be running entire fields of Thoroughbreds on Lasix in our championship races?"

Even some Thoroughbred trainers who use Lasix on their horses question the wisdom of using it on two-year-olds. But the reality is that 40 of 40 starters in the Juvenile and 29 of 30 starters in the Juvenile Filly the last three years were on Lasix the day they raced. That's 69 out of 70.

Is this to say we cannot produce more than one champion-caliber, non-bleeding two-year-old in three years?

By percentages, the Breeders' Cup race with the highest

percent of Lasix users since 1991 is the Filly & Mare Turf, which only came into existence in 1999. For three years, 34 of 40 starters in that race were on Lasix, 85.0 percent.

Of the others, the Sprint (77.2 percent) edged the Distaff (77.1 percent) and the Classic (77.0 percent) for highest Lasix usage. The Juvenile Filly was 71.1 percent, followed by the Mile (68.2 percent), the Juvenile (65.2 percent) and the Turf (59.6).

Breeders' Cup Starters Racing on Lasix

Year	Distaff	Juv. Filly	Mile	Sprint	F&M Turf	Juv.	Turf	Classic	Total	Pct
1991	8-13	5-14	7-14	5-11	-	4-14	4-13	7-11	40-90	44.4
1992	8-14	8-12	6-14	4-14	-	5-13	4-10	7-14	42-91	46.2
1993	6-8	6-8	4-13	10-14	-	9-11	6-14	5-13	46-81	56.8
1994	7-9	8-13	8-14	11-14	-	5-13	5-14	6-14	50-91	54.5
1995	7-10	4-8	7-13	7-13	-	3-13	9-13	10-11	47-81	58.0
1996	4-6	7-12	10-14	12-13	-	3-10	7-14	11-13	54-82	65.9
1997	6-8	13-14	11-12	12-14	-	7-8	9-11	9-9	67-76	88.2
1998	8-8	6-10	12-14	13-14	-	12-13	9-13	9-10	69-82	84.1
1999	7-8	9-9	13-14	14-14	14-14	14-14	11-14	14-14	93-101	92.1
2000	9-9	12-12	11-14	13-14	13-14	14-14	10-14	13-13	95-104	91.3
2001	11-11	8-9	12-12	14-14	10-12	12-12	10-11	13-13	90-94	95.7

Combined since 1991, 693 of 973 Breeders' Cup starters, 71.2 percent, raced on Lasix.

Harness racing chose a variety of different formats for its series of championship races, the Breeders Crown.

Whereas the Breeders' Cup has been held at only seven tracks (Aqueduct, Belmont, Churchill Downs, Gulfstream Park, Hollywood Park, Santa Anita and Woodbine — Arlington Park becomes the eighth host in 2002), 29 different harness tracks in North America have hosted at least one Breeders Crown race through 2001.

But that's not the only difference between the Breeders' Cup and the Breeders Crown. While Lasix use in Thoroughbreds in the Breeders' Cup has spun out of control, the Standardbreds who compete in harness racing's Breeders Crown races, especially two and three-year-olds, have mostly been Lasix-free.

From 1998 through 2001, only 63 of 420 horses in the Breeders Crown used Lasix. That's 15 percent.

Only 23 of 154 three-year-olds in the Breeders Crown those years on Lasix. That's 14.9 percent.

And of the 156 two-year-olds in the Breeders Crown from 1998 through 2001, two of 156 were on Lasix. That's 1.3 percent.

Breeders Crown Starters Racing on Lasix

Year	2YO	3YO	Older	Total	Pct.
1998	0-36	6-34	10-30	16-100	16.0
1999	0-40	4-40	10-33	14-113	12.4
2000	0-40	7-40	14-27	21-107	19.6
2001	2-40	6-40	4-20	12-100	12.0
TOTALS	2-156	23-154	38-110	63-420	15.0

Those same four years, 87 of 93 two-year-olds in the Breeders' Cup raced on Lasix, 93.5 percent.

That's an embarrassment.

Chapter 9

Disclosure, Somewhat

Monday, September 17, 1985, was a grand day for the sport of Thoroughbred racing in the Commonwealth of Kentucky. For it was on this day, at a meeting of the Kentucky State Racing Commission in Lexington, that a unanimous vote (8-0 with one commissioner absent) approved a proposal to allow the betting public to know which Thoroughbreds at its four racetracks were competing with Lasix and/or the analgesic Bute.

"It's really misinforming the public, the bettors, for them to not know which horses are on medication," Chairman Brownell Combs told Logan Bailey of the *Daily Racing Form*. "Some horses, of course, run better on it. So we feel it's the right of the betting public to know which horses are being medicated. Likewise, the public also can see which horses are being medicated for the first time."

In those three sentences, Combs should have retired the debate whether or not Lasix can improve performance, and how important first-time Lasix can be.

Earlier in his story, Bailey pointed out that horses had been running in Kentucky on furosemide and Butazolidin since the 1970s without the medication information available to the public.

So, obviously, the Kentucky State Racing Commission had not been in a rush to remedy the situation. In fact, though they passed the law in mid-September, Bailey reported that medication information would not be added to Kentucky Thoroughbred racing programs until early the following year.

71

Subsequently, on May 3, 1986, the track program listed each horse's medication in the Kentucky Derby for the first time. Of the 16 three-year-olds entered in that 112th edition of the Run for the Roses, only two raced with neither Bute nor Lasix: Ferdinand, who won the Derby for Hall of Fame trainer Charlie Whittingham and Hall of Fame jockey Bill Shoemaker, and Bold Arrangement, who finished second.

Of the other 14, Rampage, Wheatley Hall, Groovy and Wise Times (who would subsequently win the 1986 Travers at Saratoga racing without Lasix or Bute) raced with Bute and Lasix. Mogambo, Vernon Castle, third-place finisher Broad Brush, Badger Land, Snow Chief, Bachelor Beau, Icy Groom, Zabaleta and Fobby Forbes raced with Bute only. Southern Appeal raced with Lasix only.

It took the *Daily Racing Form* an additional three years to include bleeder medication — presented in paragraph form under "Kentucky Derby Medication List"— along with its past performance lines for horses in the Kentucky Derby, and more than another year to finally include medication information directly in all horses' past performance lines.

On July 1, 1990, the *Form* began using the L for Lasix and B for Bute in each horse's past performance lines for all races.

That was, obviously, after the 1990 Kentucky Derby, so the 1991 Derby was the first one in the Form with medication information listed race by race in each horse's past performance lines.

In his analysis of the 1991 Kentucky Derby, handicapper Dave Litfin pointed out just how far ahead of the learning curve he, and other sophisticated handicappers and bettors, were when he said of his choice Hansel: "Horses who race on Lasix for the second time often improve dramatically."

There had to be some readers of his analysis scratching their heads and wondering, "What the hell is Lasix?"

Chapter 10

The First Time

For Thoroughbreds, first-time Lasix is not always a ticket to the winner's circle. It improves some horses greatly, makes absolutely no difference with many and can, occasionally, hinder performance in others.

To understand Lasix's potential to improve a horse, one need only think of apprentice jockeys. If an apprentice jockey with a five-pound weight allowance has any ability, trainers are lining up to use her or him to get five pounds less weight on their Thoroughbred.

That's perfectly understandable since race secretaries assigning weight in handicap races use, as a guideline, two pounds as the equivalent of one length.

Scientific studies have proven repeatedly that the powerful diuretic effects of Lasix may cause a horse to urinate 20 pounds or more before a race. This weight loss is about the only fact of Lasix use which virtually everybody agrees on.

For handicappers, the difficulty is figuring out which horses will improve with Lasix, in either its first use or its second.

New York is apt to have more first-time Lasix users than any other racing state because not every trainer there is convinced his horses need it from Day One. And, in New York, race-day Lasix has only been allowed since September 1, 1995.

The second through fourth races at Aqueduct March 20, 2002, offered several horses who had received first-time Lasix.

In the second race, a mile and an eighth, $44,000 allowance

for non-winners of one race other than maiden, claimer or restricted, six horses entered. Three of the six showed first-time Lasix use in their past performance lines. All three went off at lower odds in their first start with Lasix.

My Cousin Matt's first-time Lasix start seemed to make little difference, though he was bet more. Without Lasix, he was second by half a length in a six-furlong maiden turf race at 4-1. With it, he was second by a length and three-quarters in a mile and a sixteenth maiden turf race at 6-5. His Beyer Speed Figure was nearly identical, 74 without Lasix and 73 with it.

Peruvian Summer had just two career starts. In his first, without Lasix, he was fourth by 4 1/2 lengths at 4-1 in a six-furlong maiden race. With Lasix in his second start, he was first by a nose at 2-1 in a mile and a sixteenth maiden race. His Beyer jumped from 55 to 74.

Cayenne Gold finished eighth by 13 1/4 lengths at 10-1 racing without Lasix in a six-furlong maiden race, earning a Beyer speed figure of 55. Stretched out to a mile and a sixteenth maiden race and given Lasix, Cayenne Gold won wire-to-wire by half a length at 2-1 with an accompanying Beyer of 79.

In the third race, a $16,500 maiden claimer ($25,000 to $35,000 claiming price) at one mile, five of the nine horses showed first-time Lasix past performance lines.

Gully Wash finished sixth by 17 1/2 lengths in his debut in a six-furlong maiden claimer at 14-1 without Lasix. With it in his second start, in the same class at the same distance, he finished third by 2 1/2 lengths at 10-1. His Beyer improved from 9 to 56.

Wings Of The Storm finished 10th by 11 3/4 lengths at 16-1 in his debut in a six-furlong maiden race at Pimlico. He dropped to a maiden claimer and added Lasix for his second career start at one mile. Bet down to 13-1, he finished third by 4 3/4 lengths, but his better performance, obviously, could be attributed to his drop in class as much as first-time Lasix. Regardless, his Beyer Figure increased from 21 to 40.

Haunted River made his debut in a six-furlong, maiden claimer at Belmont Park without Lasix. Sent off at 19-1, he finished third by 5 3/4 lengths. He stretched out to a mile for his next start at Aqueduct with Lasix added in a slightly higher maiden claimer, was bet down to 7-2 and finished seventh by 26 lengths. His Beyer decreased from a 43 to 14.

Ring Of Thunder finished eighth by 24 1/4 lengths at 25-1 in his debut in a six-furlong maiden race at Aqueduct. Shipped to softer company at Tampa Bay Downs, he stretched out to a seven-furlong maiden race with the addition of Lasix. Bet down to 6-1, he finished third by 10 1/4 lengths, improving his Beyer from 9 to 33.

Finally, Ms. Wolf had been second in her debut at 5-2 in a 4 1/2-furlong maiden claimer at Delaware Park. She made her second start on the grass at Belmont Park in a maiden special weights at 6-1 and finished seventh. Returned to dirt and dropped back to a six-furlong, maiden claimer at Delaware Park at the same level as her debut, she added Lasix and finished second by seven lengths at 7-2. Her Beyer on dirt was 52, compared to the 39 she ran in her first start.

In the fourth race, a mile and an eighth, $46,000 allowance for New York-Breds who had not won two races, two of six horses had past performance lines with first-time Lasix.

Lilt was sixth by 18 lengths at 9-2 in a New York-Bred stakes race at six furlongs without Lasix, then seventh by 11 lengths at 6-1 with Lasix in a six-furlong New York-Bred maiden race at Belmont Park. His Beyer improved from 27 to 45.

Huntcountrycorner was 11th by 21 lengths at 20-1 without Lasix in a six-furlong New York-Bred allowance race for non-winners of two. With Lasix, in the same class at the same distance, he was fifth by nine lengths at 19-1. His Beyer rocketed from a 30 to a 66.

The conclusions from 10 sample horses is that first-time Lasix helped several, some significantly, and appeared to hinder Haunted River. Eight of the 10 improved their Beyer speed figure.

The next day at Aqueduct, March 21, 2002, there were 23 horses who had raced on Lasix for the first-time in their past performance lines.

Fourteen of the 23 showed improvement on first-time Lasix; seven showed little change, and two regressed.

Of the 14 who showed improvement, six took a major step forward:

Perty Number's last two starts were both in a mile and a sixteenth, New York-Bred allowance company for non-winners of two races. He was fourth by 13 3/4 lengths at 7-1 without Lasix, then second by half a length at 4-1 with it. His Beyer improved from 50 to 64.

Condo Prison was third by 5 3/4 lengths in a maiden claimer at Arlington Park without Lasix at 8-1, then won a maiden claimer at Churchill Downs by half a length with Lasix at 3-1.

Mesolithic finished 12th by 20 lengths at 17-1 in a New York-Bred maiden race without Lasix, then fourth by 8 1/4 lengths at 6-1 with it in the same condition.

Celera was ninth by 11 1/4 lengths at 34-1 without Lasix in a $60,000 maiden claimer, then dropped to a maiden $25,000 claimer, added Lasix, and won by a length and a quarter at 17-1, improving his Beyer from 36 to 52.

It's A Monster was second by half a length at 3-1 in his debut at Laurel Lasix-free, then won his second start by 7 1/4 lengths at Laurel running for purse money only with Lasix.

Dusting Of Powder's debut and second career start were both six-furlong maiden races for New York-Breds at Aqueduct. Without Lasix, he was fifth by 10 1/2 lengths at 27-1. With Lasix, he was second by a neck at 8-5, even though his Beyer only improved from 43 to 45.

The two who regressed were Diablo's Caper, who was third by nine lengths without Lasix at 6-1, then eighth by 14 lengths at 15-1 with it, and Winter Sport, who was third by 2 3/4 lengths at 13-1 without Lasix in an open company maiden race, and then, in the same class and at the same distance, fifth by 7 1/4 lengths at 5-1 with Lasix with a Beyer drop from 50 to 45.

Let's look at one more day at Aqueduct, March 22, 2002. Thirty horses entered showed first-time Lasix in their past performance lines. Of those 30, 23 showed improvement, six showed little change and one regressed.

Of the 23 who improved, 17 improved significantly, including:

Place Kicker — She was second by 8 3/4 lengths without Lasix at 6-1 and first by three lengths at 9-5 with it. Both starts were maiden route races.

Tight Wire — She was ninth by 18 1/2 lengths in a maiden sprint at Philadelphia Park at 86-1 sans Lasix, then third by 7 3/4 lengths in a maiden route at the same track at 82-1 with it. Her Beyer improved from 15 to 39.

Frisky Kitty — After running ninth by 17 1/2 lengths at 17-1 in a maiden race at Keeneland without Lasix, she shipped to Aqueduct, added Lasix, and finished third by 4 1/2 lengths at 8-1, upping her Beyer from 34 to 59.

Hitchin' Post — In a mile and an eighth maiden race at Belmont Park, he was fourth by 19 3/4 lengths at 5-1 without Lasix. With it in a 1 1/16 mile-maiden race at Belmont Park, he was second by 3 3/4 lengths at 10-1.

Jam Down Queen — Her first two career starts were in maiden $25,000 claimers at six furlongs at Aqueduct. Debuting without Lasix, she was seventh by 13 1/4 lengths at 38-1. With Lasix, she was second by 4 3/4 lengths at 2-1 as her Beyer jumped from 25 to 46.

But Lasix did not help Really Something. In identical races, a six-furlong, New York-Bred non-winners of two allowance, she was fourth by 4 3/4 lengths at 7-1 without Lasix, then sixth by 15 3/4 lengths with it at 6-1 as her Beyer dropped from 64 to 45.

Obviously, in every single race, there are dozens of factors which can affect a horse's performance besides the addition of

Lasix, be it a change in distance, class, surface, jockey, weight, blinkers, etc.

But can anyone open the *Daily Racing Form*, look at horses with past performance lines which include the first-time use of Lasix, and conclude that Lasix does not alter performance?

Could you look at Silver Seraph and not make that conclusion? Without Lasix in a New York-bred maiden route race, she finished eighth by 16 lengths at 20-1 on January 4, 2002, at Aqueduct. With Lasix under the same conditions, March 8, 2002, at Aqueduct, she was second by a length and three-quarters at 18-1.

Some horses improve in their second start on Lasix, though bettors obviously didn't think they would in these two examples:

In his first three career starts, all six-furlong New York-bred maiden races at Aqueduct in February and March, 2002, Bags Are Packed was 10th by 19 3/4 lengths at 21-1 in his Lasix-less debut; seventh by 10 1/2 lengths at 25-1 with Lasix, then third by two lengths at 24-1 in his second start on Lasix. His Beyers went from 26 to 39 to 49.

Grandstandsuperman's first three career starts were also in six-furlong New York-Bred maiden races in January and February at Aqueduct. Without Lasix in his debut, he was seventh by 17 1/2 lengths at 40-1. With first-time Lasix, he was ninth by 19 1/2 lengths at 31-1, and, on second-time Lasix, second by half a length at 66-1. His Beyers were 30, 27 and 64, respectively.

Sugar-coating horses' improvement on Lasix by saying they were only running to their true ability does not change the fact that their performances were enhanced, even as a couple first-time Lasix horses ran worse and many others showed little change.

Lasix can alter horses' performance big-time, and every handicapper in America takes notice when a horse gets Lasix for the first time. The hard part is figuring out which horses Lasix will improve the most.

As a general rule, it seems that first-time Lasix helps front-running horses who have been stopping. For example, Michael's

Temper was in two consecutive six-furlong maiden races for two-year-old New York-Breds at Aqueduct in November, 2001. On Nov. 3, he made the lead, weakened and finished third by 2 1/2 lengths at 10-1. With Lasix 19 days later, he won by 10 1/4 lengths at 6-5, improving his Beyer from 58 to 77.

Examining a trainer's track record with first-time Lasix horses can only help handicappers. The following table shows the numbers and percentages of trainers around the country who have used first-time Lasix at least once between Jan. 1, 2000, and Dec. 31, 2001, excluding their final 2001 start.

Lasix Trainers

• Winners, starters and percentages with first-time Lasix for 2000 and 2001

Louisa Acuna, 0-3

Paul Aguirre, 3-22, 13.6 %

Ferris Allen, 9-70, 12.9 %

Tom Amoss, 11-68, 16.2 %

James Anderson, 0-3

Robert Anderson, 2-18, 11.1 %

Roger Anderson, 0-10

Susan Anderson, 0-4

George Angelopos, 1-6, 16.7 %

Rene Araya, 0-11

George Arnold, 8-74, 10.8 %

Richard Arnold, Jr., 3-24, 12.5 %

David Asbury, 0-16

Steve Asmussen, 58-225, 25.8 %

Roger Attfield, 9-66, 13.6 %

Edward Auwarter, 0-8

Joseph Ayres, 1-5, 20.0 %

Leo Azpurua, Jr., 8-34, 23.5 %

Manuel Azpurua, 0-8

Billy Badgett, 2-41, 4.9 %

Bob Baffert, 29-182, 15.9 %

Arnold Bardin, 0-8

Edward Barker, 0-6

Kenneth Barnardo, 0-2

Bobby Barnett, 8-64, 12.5 %

Luis Barrera, 0-7

Oscar Barrera, Jr., 1-10, 10.0 %

Paul Barrow, 6-16, 37.5 %

Larry Bates, 1-21, 4.8 %

Anthony Battaglia, 0-3

Robert Bean, 0-8

Stephanie Beattie, 0-1

Rafael Becerra, 0-14

Bruno Bellucci, 2-13, 15.4 %

Howard Belvoir, 5-39, 12.8 %

Manuel Berrios, 0-16

Eli Betancourt, Jr., 1-10, 10.0 %

Pascha Bignault, 2-18, 11.1 %

Danny Bird, 0-13

Chris Block, 7-31, 22.6 %

Kevin Boniface, 1-19, 5.3 %

Allen Borosh, 1-7, 14.3 %

Keith Bourgeois, 11-79, 13.9 %

Jerry Bozzo, 0-4

Vince Bracciale, 2-4, 50.0 %

David Bradley, 10-35, 28.6 %

Samuel Breaux, 3-42, 7.1 %

Kelly Breen, 3-25, 12.0 %

Denzil Brooks, 0-2

Frank Brothers, 6-32, 18.8 %

Kelly Broussard, 1-17, 5.9 %

William Brownlee, 0-8

George Brunacini, 0-3

Jonathan Buckley, 2-23, 8.7 %

Paul Buttigieg, 2-18, 11.1 %

Don Cain, 1-3, 33.3 %

Joe Cain, 2-26, 7.7 %

Joseph Calascibetta, 4-46, 8.7 %

William Calhoun, 3-33, 11.1 %

Alfredo Callejas, 0-9

Arturo Calva, 0-8

Ray Cameon, 0-3

John Campo, Jr., 0-24

Christopher Candies, 5-37. 13.5 %

John Candlin, 0-6

Julian Canet, 9-42, 21.4 %

Gary Capuano, 6-28. 21.4 %

Jack Carava, 5-30, 16.7 %

Charles Carlesimo Kr., 0-7

David Carroll, 2-24, 8.3 %

Del Carroll, 1-32, 3.1 %

Henry Carroll, 4-17, 23.5 %

Stephen Casey, 1-6, 16.7 %

Mark Casse, 20-124, 15.1 %

Michael Catalano, 1-8, 12.5 %

Joseph Catanese, 2-13, 15.4 %

Lewis Cenicola, 0-11

Vladimir Cerin, 11-52, 21.2 %

Jim Chandler, 0-1
William Cheff, 1-4, 25.0 %
Matthew Chew, 0-8
Lucy Childress, 0-2
William Christmas, 0-4
Richard Ciardullo, 5-31, 15.1 %
Gene Cilio, 10-54, 18.5 %
Paul Cimini, 0-2
Christophe Clement, 23-112, 20.5 %
Henry Cochran, 4-11, 36.4 %
Marialice Coffey, 0-4
Henry Collazo, 2-19, 10.5 %
William Connelly, 3-23, 13.0 %
Gary Contessa, 7-70, 10.0 %
Javier Contreras, 5-33, 15.2 %
Ray Correa, 0-1
Gary Cortolillo, 2-4, 50.0 %
Luis Cotto, 0-1
Warren Croll, Jr. 1-17, 5.9 %
Kathleen Crook Demasi, 4-28, 14.3 %
Michael Crowder, 2-10, 20.0 %
William Currin, 0-9
Dee Curry, 3-9, 33.3 %
Richard Czerwonka, 0-3
James Danaher, 2-5, 40.0 %
James Day, 1-6, 16.7 %
Jose De Lima, 0-12
Denise Delmonte, 0-2
Bud Delp, 9-48, 18.8 %
Carl Deville, 3-32, 0.4 %
Edgar Diaz, 1-3, 33.3 %
Damon Dilodovico, 0-6
Elaine Di Marsico, 0-3
Stephen DiMauro, 8-45, 17.8 %
Glenn Disanto, 1-2, 50.0 %
James DiVito, 2-18, 11.1 %
Carl Domino, 3-12, 25.0 %
David Donk, 3-25, 12.0 %
Michael Doyle, 3-43, 7.0 %
Ed Drivinghawk, Jr., 0-1
Neil Drysdale, 14-84, 16.7 %
Anthony Dutrow, 19-66, 28.8 %
Richard Dutrow, 8-22, 36.4 %

Kristina Dupps, 1-5, 20.0 %
Oliver Edwards, 3-17, 17.6 %
Hassan Elamri, 0-2
Ron Ellis, 4-45, 8.9 %
Chris Englehart, 1-9, 11.1 %
Jesus Enriquez, 1-28, 3.6 %
Mary Eppler, 3-38, 7.9 %
Manuel Estevez, 1-15, 6.7 %
Annette Eubanks, 2-11, 18.2 %
Scott Everett, 2-9, 22.2 %
Patricia Fagan, 0-2
James Fanara, 0-1
Patricia Farro, 1-14, 7.3 %
John Fee, 0-8
Jim Ferraro, 0-8
Mike Ferraro, 6-16, 37.5 %
James Finegan, 0-1
William Fires, 2-33, 6.1 %
Bernie Flint, 21-94, 22.3 %
Ernest Flynn, 0-12
David Forster, 6-43, 14.0 %
Paul Fout, 2-6, 33.3 %
Murray Frazier, 0-5
Willard Freeman, 0-3
Mitch Friedman, 0-9
Kenyon Furlong, 0-2
Dominic Galluscio, 3-20, 15.0 %
Ernest Ganfield, 5-33, 15.2 %
Efrain Garcia, 0-1
Juan Garcia, 4-49, 8.2 %
Rudolfo Garcia, 3-21, 14.3 %
Janice Gerace, 1-22, 4.5 %
Norbert Gerber, 0-1
Barry Germany, 5-23, 21.7 %
Alan Goldberg, 10-41, 24.4 %
Mickey Goldfine, 1-13, 7.7 %
Frank Gomez, 10-53, 18.9 %
Terrel Gore, 1-18, 5.6 %
Michael Gorham, 4-26, 15.4 %
Donna Green, 1-4, 25.0 %
Thomas Greene, 1-16, 6.7 %
Sam Greenslate, 0-2
Phillip Grimm, Jr., 0-3

Bessie Gruwell, 2-7, 28.6 %
Jorge Gutierrez, 0-10
Charles Hadry, 4-21, 19.0 %
Jerry Hardin, 3-15, 20.0 %
Holly Harris, 1-3, 33.3 %
Mary Hartman, 5-17, 29.4 %
Phil Hauswald, 1-21, 4.8 %
Charles Hawkins, 0-2
Phil Hauswald, 1-19, 5.3 %
Jennifer Hayford, 0-5
Richard Hazelton, 8-45, 17.8 %
Bruce Headley, 1-23, 4.3 %
Thomas Heard, 0-8
William Hedus, 0-5
Mark Hennig, 19-99, 19.2 %
Ramon Hernandez, 4-24, 16.7 %
Russell Herold, 0-2
John Hertler, 3-23, 13.0 %
Rick Hiles, 1-5, 20.0 %
Timothy Hills, 11-53, 20.8 %
Steve Hobby, 1-25, 4.0 %
Robert Holman, 1-14, 7.1 %
Larry Holt, 3-17, 17.6 %
Rosemary Homeister, Sr., 2-13, 15.4 %
Neil Howard, 9-36, 25.0 %
Daniel Hurtak, 3-24, 12.5 %
Mike Hushion, 12-44, 27.3 %
Joe Imperio, 0-7
Leonard Imperio, 0-10
Eduardo Inda, 3-19, 15.8 %
Sal Iorio, 2-6, 33.3 %
Abdulla Ishaq, 0-1
Alan Iwinski, 18-65, 27.7 %
Ellen Jackson, 1-27, 3.7 %
Diane Jeanmont, 0-4
Charles Jenda, 8-69, 11.6 %
Allen Jerkens, 4-19, 21.1 %
Jimmy Jerkens, 2-13, 15.4 %
Deborah Johnson, 1-4, 25.0 %
P.G. Johnson, 2-28, 7.1%
Jack Jones, Jr., 1-2, 50.5 %
Harold Jordan, Jr., 0-6
Barbara Kees, 1-5, 20.0 %

Dennis Kelley, 0-2
John Kelly, 2-6, 33.3 %
Pat Kelly, 3-16, 18.8 %
John Kimmel, 19-115, 16.5 %
Bob Klesaris, 1-17, 5.9 %
Duane Knipe, 1-12, 8.3 %
Paul Kopaj, 0-2
Frank Laboccetta, Jr., 0-1
Armando Lage, 3-48, 6.3 %
Scott Lake, 6-27, 22.2 %
William Lazuka, 0-1
King Leatherbury, 4-30, 13.3 %
Jeanne Leblanc, 0-1
Michael Lecesse, 0-7
Frank Leggio, 2-13, 15.4 %
Michael Lenzini, 4-24, 16.7 %
Robert Leonard, 1-3, 33.3 %
Roy Lerman, 0-5
Bob Levine, 1-6, 16.7 %
Bruce Levine, 1-23, 4.3 %
Betty Loter, 0-5
Lawrence Lotze, 0-3
Frank Lucarelli, 7-65, 10.8 %
Richard Lugovich, 0-2
D. Wayne Lukas, 18-164, 11.0 %
Richard Lundy, 1-22, 4.5 %
Roland Mabe, 0-1
Michael Machowsky, 6-40, 15.0 %
Patricia Manahan, 0-1
Dennis Manning, 4-26, 15.4 %
Robert Manning, 0-8
William March, 0-2
Carlos Martin, 4-31, 12.9 %
Gregory Martin, 0-6
Ramon Martin, 2-13, 15.4 %
Michael Matz, 5-38, 13.2 %
Ron McAnally, 15-83, 18.1 %
Tim McCanna, 12-64, 18.8 %
Greg McCarron, 0-9
Jerry McClarney, 0-4
Michael McDonald, 1-16, 6.3 %
Shug McGaughey, 8-38, 21.0 %
Paul McGee, 8-47, 17.0 %

Jerry McGrath, 1-3, 33.3 %
Andrew McKeever, 2-12, 16.7 %
Michael McKinnell, 0-3
Lee McKinney, 0-3
James McMullen, 0-12
Ken McPeek, 10-59, 16.9 %
Angel Medina, 0-11
Pastore Mena III, 0-1
Ann Merryman, 4-15, 26.7 %
Lou Mettinis, 1-8, 12.5 %
Michael Miceli, 0-15
Rory Miller, 0-6
Gretchen Mobberley, 2-6, 33.3 %
Angel Montano, 3-27, 11.1 %
Gerasimos Moschonas, 0-2
Graham Motion, 19-99, 19.2 %
Billy Mott, 30-131, 22.9 %
William Myers, 2-24, 8.3 %
Carl Nafzger, 8-39, 20.5 %
John Nazarath, 0-6
Kathleen Nelson, 0-2
Harry Neville, 0-5
Andrew Ney, 2-10, 20.0 %
Larry Nibarger, 0-2
Randy Nunley, 3-23, 13.0 %
Colum O'Briend, 0-12
Leo O'Brien, 5-42, 11.9 %
Niall O'Callaghan, 3-53, 5.7 %
Kathleen O'Connell, 14-81, 17.3 %
Duane Offield, 1-23, 4.3 %
Luis Olivares, 3-35, 8.6 %
Jerry Orm, 0-2
Joe Orseno, 7-32, 21.9 %
Phil Oviedo, 1-12, 8.3 %
Lloyd Palmer, 1-1, 100.0 %
John Paone, 0-2
Robert Parker, 0-8
Albert Parody, 0-2
Dan Peitz, 2-16, 12.5 %
Walter Peltier, 1-2, 50.0 %
Angel Penna, Jr., 3-18, 16.7 %
Ben Perkins, Jr., 14-42, 33.3 %
William Perry, 5-27, 18.5 %

Kenneth Person, 0-2
Jim Picou, 0-7
Larry Pilotti, 12-59, 20.3 %
Michael Pino, 1-24, 4.2 %
Ed Plesa, 0-2
Ed Plesa, Jr., 10-70, 14.3 %
Todd Pletcher, 26-146, 17.8 %
Norman Pointer, 1-26, 3.8 %.
Terri Pompay, 4-22, 18.2 %
Douglas Potter, 1-4, 25.0 %
Dee Poulos, 0-10
John Pregman, Jr., 0-7
John Quiles, 0-5
Marcos Rangel, 0-1
Faustino Ramos, 2-14, 14.3 %
Todd Rarik, 1-19, 5.3 %
Robert Raymond, 4-30, 13.3 %
Michael Rea, 0-9
Walter Reese, 4-20, 20.0 %
Allison Register, 0-4
Robert Reid, Jr., 0-5
Bob Reinacher Jr., 4-12, 33.3 %
Anthony Reinstedler, 6-37, 16.2 %
Linda Rice, 13-74, 17.6 %
Willie Riley, 0-4
Robert Ringhoff, 2-10. 20.0 %
Tim Ritchey, 9-42, 21.4 %
Timothy Ritvo, 8-67, 11.9 %
Miguel Rivera, 1-4, 25.0 %
Juan Rizo, 4-19, 21.0 %
Stanley Roberts, 1-29, 3.4 %
David Rodriguez, 3-6, 50.0 %
Barry Roos, 0-4
Richard Root, 1-13, 7.7 %
Harold Rose, 1-11, 9.1 %
Louie Roussel III, 3-16, 18.8 %
Steve Rowan, 2-11, 18.2 %
Derek Ryan, 1-24, 4.2 %
James Ryerson, 2-16, 12.5 %
Anthony Saavedra, 0-15
Greg Sacco, 0-15
Jenine Sahadi, 11-35, 31.4 %
Angel Salinas, 9-58, 15.5 %

John Salzman, 6-30, 20.0 %
Thomas Sam, 0-5
Gaston Sandoval, 1-13, 7.7 %
Merrill Scherer, 3-20, 15.0 %
Richard Scherer, 4-26, 15.4 %
Dominick Schettino, 0-16
Paul Schiewe, 1-7, 14.3 %
Scotty Schulhofer, 7-27, 25.9 %
Rick Schosberg, 8-34, 23.5 %
Scotty Schulhofer, 7-28, 25.0 %
Jayd Schuyler, 0-7
Scott Schwartz, 5-16, 31.2 %
Paul Seefeldt, 3-12, 25.0 %
Robert Seeger, 5-36, 13.9 %
Alan Seewald, 3-21, 14.3 %
Kearney Segura, 0-11, 19.4 %
Phil Serpe, 6-31, 19.4 %
John Servis, 6-25, 24.0 %
Frank Shannon, 1-9, 11.1 %
Jonathan Sheppard, 10-67, 14.9 %
Thomas Short, 0-7
Sanford Shulman, 2-28, 7.1
Ray Shumake, 0-2
Alvin Sider, 0-4
Charles Simon, 4-33, 12.1 %
Tom Skiffington, 1-17, 5.9 %
Richard Small, 1-16, 6.2 %
Ernest Smith, 1-2, 50.0 %
Franklin Smith, 3-24, 12.5 %
Harold Smith, 22-87, 25.3 %
Jere R Smith Sr., 1-14, 7.1 %
Kenny Smith, 10-88, 11.4 %
Dan Smithwick, 3-19, 15.8 %
Daryl Snow, 0-5
Gerald Souto, 0-2
Ronald Spatz, 4-37, 10.9 %
Frank Springer, 0-9
Steve Standridge, 7-40, 17.5 %
Kate St. Leon, 3-18, 16.7 %
Dallas Stewart, 15-118, 12.7 %
Michael Stidham, 17-98, 17.3 %
Uriah St. Lewis, 0-25
Lance Stokes, 1-27, 3.7 %

Richard Stoklosa, 0-14
Clinton Stuart, 9-35, 25.8 %
Warren Stute, 3-16, 18.8 %
Brent Sumja, 9-45, 20.0 %
Michael Tammaro, 3-39, 7.7 %
Herman Taylor, 2-19, 10.5 %
John Terranova, 3-16, 18.8 %
Howie Tesher, 2-18, 11.1 %
Valora Testerman, 3-25, 12.0 %
Jamey Thomas, 1-9, 11.1 %
Phil Thomas, Jr., 0-1
Glenn Thompson, 0-2
Willard Thompson, 4-39, 10.3 %
Yvette Thompson, 0-7
Michael Tomlinson, 5-23, 21.7%
Jim Toner, 5-35, 14.3
Adolfo Torres, 0-1
Emanuel Tortora, 11-82, 13.4 %
Steve Towne, 4-22, 18.2 %
Richard Trimmer, 1-10, 10.0 %
Robert Triola, 1-9, 11.1 %
Michael Trivigno, 1-18, 5.6%
Jeff Trosclair, 3-10, 30.0 %
Billy Turner, 2-19, 10.5 %
Woodford Tuttle, 1-1, 100.0 %
Jack Van Berg, 2-44, 4.5 %
Thomas Van Berg, 2-37, 5.4 %
David Vance, 1-34, 2.9 %
Harvey Vanier, 2-44, 4.5 %
Jacinto Vasquez, 1-7, 14.3 %
Richard Vega, 3-21, 14.3 %
John Veitch, 0-1
Alfredo Velazquez, 1-17, 5.9 %
Peter Vestal, 4-11, 3.6 %
Patrick Victoria, 0-1
Rick Violette, 4-30, 13.3 %
David Vivian, 6-24, 25.0 %
Don Von Hemel, 5-36, 13.9 %
Jeanne Vuyosevich, 0-2
Kenneth Wade, 0-1
Elliott Walden, 12-129, 9.3 %
Thomas Walsh, 1-6, 16.7 %
Wesley Ward, 11-46, 23.9 %

Doyle Wardrop, 0-5
Ronnie Warren, 0-1
Christine Wasilewski, 0-3
Ann Watermeier, 0-5
Robert Werner, 0-4
Ronnie Werner, 15-59, 25.4 %
Eugene Weymouth, 4-29, 13.8 %
Clarke Whitaker, 0-8
Donald White, 0-6
William White, 29-128, 22.7 %
Lynn Whiting, 3-23, 13.0 %
Mark Whitton, 0-10
Hal Wiggins, 9-62, 14.5 %
Jesse Wigginton, 2-8, 25.0 %
Bryan Wilkins, 1-4, 25.0 %
Donald Winfree, 2-16, 12.5 %
Martin Wolfson, 5-32, 15.6 %
Milton Wolfson, 2-17, 11.8 %
Jackie Wright, 3-9, 33.3 %
James Wright, 0-2
Gene York, 2-5, 40.0 %
Arthur Zeis, 0-10
Jon Zimmerman, 0-12
Nick Zito, 9-103, 8.7 %

• According to the *Daily Racing Form* —
Does not include final 2001 start

Chapter 11

The Controversy Percolates

While the number of racing states allowing Lasix on race day continued to grow through the 1980s — by 1985, only three of the major 23 Thoroughbred racing states, Arizona, Arkansas and New York, did not allow it — those against it stood their ground.

Accompanying a five-part 1985 series on Lasix by Deirdre B. Biles in *The Blood-Horse*, the magazine it publishes, the Thoroughbred Owners and Breeders Association reiterated its stand on all race-day medication, not only Lasix.

In an Editor's Note atop the first part of the series, TOBA said:

"The trustees of the Thoroughbred Owners and Breeders Association, publishers of *The Blood-Horse*, recently voted to reaffirm the position originally stated in 1977 'opposing the use of medication of any kind for racing purposes.' The TOBA, *The Blood-Horse* and a number of other organizations in racing generally have supported that stance for many years. They include the National Association of State Racing Commissioners, which still has in place its recommendation prohibiting race-day medication.

"Nevertheless, like it or not, the vast majority of racing is conducted under rules which allow horses to race on the bleeder medication furosemide (Lasix). Twenty of the 23 major states allow Lasix, and they account for 82 percent of the purse money provided by Thoroughbred racing.

"Ongoing research is redefining what a bleeder is, and

additional research is geared towards determining what causes a horse to bleed. Thus, the thought here is, that despite having stated categorically opposition to race-day medication in the past, it is appropriate to review various aspects of the question again. In the accompanying article, and those to follow, opinions of trainers, researchers, veterinarians, racing regulators, will be aired.

"Another reason for the racing industry to frequently re-examine the question of medication is that Congress periodically does so. The Humane Society attitude, as stated by field investigator Robert Baker (the author of "The Misuse of Drugs in Horse Racing") recently is, 'I think that the horse racing industry, realizing that it has not cleaned up its act, will now argue that these drugs are not harmful after all.'

"Baker said that, since the last round of federal regulation bills were fended off four years ago, 'Eighteen states have relaxed their medication rules,' and he interprets such statistics as confirming the suspicion 'that the industry lacks sincerity in trying to clean up horse racing.' This will be 'very compelling to Congress,' Baker warned.

"Thus the Lasix issue, while old and perplexing, does not lie easily under the rug, from whatever vantage point it is swept."

Integrity did matter to some. In January, 1986, by a 4-1 vote, the Maryland Racing Commission took a stand against Lasix, prohibiting it for the Preakness Stakes at Pimlico and the Washington, D.C., International at Laurel. But a month later, following intense lobbying by management at the two tracks and by the Horsemen's Benevolent and Protective Association, the state's Administrative, Executive and Legislative Review Committee rejected the rule change.

"The commission was for it, but everyone else was against it," J. Michael Hopkins, the assistant secretary of the Maryland Racing Commission, told Jay Hovdey, then with the *New York Times.* "The premise for the Grade 1 stakes is that they truly prove which of the breed is best. The board believes it should be done without medication."

Races without horses on Lasix were becoming an endangered species in Maryland by the end of the 1980s. In 1980, 218 Thoroughbreds raced on Lasix. By 1989, the number was 12,585. Lasix in Standardbreds had climbed from 720 in 1985 to 5,018 in 1989.

Maryland By The Numbers

Year	Thoroughbreds on Lasix	Standardbreds on Lasix
1980	218	
1981	952	
1982	1,328	
1983	2,121	
1984	3,484	
1985	4,329	720
1986	5,738	3,086
1987	7,299	3,983
1988	10,299	4,354
1989	12,585	5,018

Source — The Maryland Racing Commission's 17th Annual Report (1989)

Hovdey's May 14, 1986, story about the Maryland Racing Commission also quoted Rick Norton, director of the Kentucky Racing Commission, who offered a different perspective. "It has been documented that around 80 percent of all racehorses are bleeders to some degree," he said. "There is an honest purpose to the use of such medication. States like New York and Maryland are sweeping it under the rug if they don't deal with it."

Norton did not stop there. He also took credit for his

commission's decision to print medication information in racetrack programs. "The commission feels such a disclosure eliminates the suspicion that some information is being held back from the public," he said.

He didn't tell Hovdey why it had taken Kentucky roughly a decade to come to that decision.

Hovdey's story was full of interesting Lasix information. Trainer Jerry Fanning told Hovdey how he and the owners of Desert Wine went to court to allow Desert Wine to race on Lasix in the 1983 Preakness, after finishing second with Lasix in the Kentucky Derby. Maryland racing officials had told Desert Wine's connections that he did not qualify as a Maryland bleeder because a Maryland state veterinarian had not personally observed a post-race hemorrhage. So they went to court to get an injunction.

"The judge was a runner who had asthma," Fanning told Hovdey. "He didn't see the difference between a human taking medication to help him breathe while he competed and a horse using Lasix to prevent bleeding."

Fanning added this comment: "Anyway, those trainers back there told me how they got on the bleeder list whenever they wanted to. Just took a syringe full of blood, stuck it up a horse's nostril and showed him to the state vet."

In 1987, Lasix was hot news again, commanding an even bigger national spotlight throughout and after that year's Triple Crown.

Alysheba, a son of Alydar who raced on Lasix, won the Kentucky Derby and the Preakness over Bet Twice, who finished second in both races by less than a length.

In the Belmont Stakes, Alysheba would seek to become the first Triple Crown winner since Affirmed defeated Alydar in all three legs of the Triple Crown in 1978. But Alysheba, and all his opponents, would have to compete in the Belmont Stakes without Lasix. New York State would not allow Lasix until Sept. 1, 1995.

Bet Twice not only denied Alysheba the Triple Crown, but

won the Belmont Stakes by 14 lengths over Cryptoclearance, who beat Gulch by a nose for second. Alysheba, who'd gotten into traffic trouble twice under Hall of Famer Chris McCarron, was another neck back in fourth.

To his considerable credit, Alysheba's Hall of Fame trainer, Jack Van Berg, did not use Lasix as an excuse. He even went so far as to share with the public the results of an endoscopic examination of Alysheba after the race. Alysheba had not bled from exercise-induced pulmonary hemorrhaging in the running of the Belmont.

But the matter was far from over.

For as racing fans eagerly awaited the next match-up of the two stars in the Haskell Invitational at Monmouth Park, Aug. 1, Bet Twice's trainer, Jimmy Croll, threatened to skip the race if Alysheba was allowed to use Lasix that day.

Alysheba was qualified to use Lasix in the Haskell because New Jersey and Maryland had a reciprocal agreement regarding Lasix, and Alysheba had raced on Lasix in the Preakness.

Croll objected because New Jersey also had a rule that bleeders must be seen to qualify for Lasix, and Maryland officials had not witnessed Alysheba bleeding, but allowed him to use Lasix because he had raced on the medication in California. New Jersey did not recognize the bleeders list in California (or in Kentucky, the only two states New Jersey did not recognize), so Croll felt Alysheba should not be allowed Lasix in the Haskell.

"He wasn't examined in Maryland," Croll said. "The mere fact that he (Alysheba) raced in Maryland makes him eligible, so the rule is interpreted very poorly. I think it should be changed. This is why I protested. If you never say anything, you never get it done. So I made a little noise."

Apparently, Van Berg had heard enough noise about Lasix. A week before the Haskell, he declared that Alysheba would race without Lasix. "I'm sick of hearing about Lasix," Van Berg told Clive Gammon in an Aug. 10, 1987, story in *Sports Illustrated*. "We're going to the Travers (on Aug. 22) and they don't run on

Lasix up there. So it's better for the horse and better for the public if we run without it this time."

There was yet another point of view on Lasix by the legitimate third contender in the Haskell, Lost Code. who had won seven straight stakes. Since being treated with Lasix by trainer Bill Donovan, Lost Code was undefeated.

"Lasix has been a godsend to me," Donovan told Gammon. "Ban it? Hey, I'm a horseman. I make my living doing this. When you have to make a living out of these bums, you have to do whatever you have to to win. It's almost as if the Lord came down and said, 'Bill, I'm going to put my arm around you, son, and put you out of your misery.' Thirty years I've sweated and hustled, drove vans all night, ponied horses all day, mucked stalls, hotwalked horses, broke yearlings, got thrown, stomped, bit and kicked, traveled all the leaky roof circuits from Ellis Park to Jefferson Downs to Shenandoah to Waterford. It wasn't so easy. This is better." Donovan gave Lost Code Lasix after he "gushed blood all over the floor, all over the walls of his stall," after a race in Alabama. "I ran him in Birmingham on Lasix for the first time, and he won impressively," Donovan said. "So I've kept him on it ever since. How could I change?"

Gammon's Haskell story in *Sports Illustrated* also quoted other trainers. Bud Delp, who trained Spectacular Bid and was one of the first Maryland trainers to use Lasix, said, "I ran every single horse I trained on Lasix. Every single solitary one. I had no problems and I won a lot of races. Yeah, Lasix gives them a lift."

Hall of Fame California trainer Charlie Whittingham said the exact opposite: "Lasix doesn't move a horse up at all. That is what the press thinks. It just stops him from bleeding. Heck, sometimes it'll run worse."

Hall of Fame New York trainer Mack Miller offered his perspective, "Lasix may be the greatest thing in the world for bleeders, but you cannot have it in one state and not in another. It's not fair to the public, and it's the public that makes this thing go."

Gammon did also mention the actual running of the Haskell in *Sports Illustrated*. Bet Twice beat Alysheba by a neck with Lost Code just another neck behind in third. Gammon wrote, "After Alysheba's second-place finish in the Haskell, a feisty Van Berg announced, 'Anybody says anything about Lasix and I'll get up and swing at him. I'll hit him straight in the nose.' His aggravation is understandable — but surely there's a better solution."

No kidding. Horse racing rarely gets non-Triple Crown or Breeders' Cup coverage in *Sports Illustrated*. But instead of a story focusing on what turned out to be a fantastic three-horse battle to the wire, people were reading about Lasix, trying to make sense out of a situation that has never made sense even to racing fans. Gammon's story also touched upon the lack of uniformity from state to state in not only their rules about Lasix, but also their policy of disclosure of Lasix information to the betting public.

This helped racing's image?

Bet Twice and Alysheba met again in the $1 million Travers and neither hit the board as Mack Miller's Java Gold won on an extremely sloppy track. Bet Twice was fifth, and Alysheba sixth by 20 1/4 lengths.

So, in his two starts in New York without Lasix, Alysheba had finished a distant fourth in the Belmont Stakes and an even worse sixth in the Travers.

Yet Alysheba returned to New York the following year and won the Grade 1 Woodward Stakes by a neck over Forty Niner on the way to being named 1988 Horse of the Year. Without Lasix.

Then he retired. The controversy over Lasix did not.

In 1989 in California, Assemblyman Dick Floyd introduced the Free Racing Bill, calling for the prohibition of all medication, including Lasix, within 48 hours of race time. The bill passed the Assembly, but languished in the Senate, where it did not have the vital support of State Senate Minority Leader Ken Maddy, a former hotwalker and groom who later owned Thoroughbreds.

Racing without drugs? Floyd was California dreamin.'

But the racing industry clamored for an answer in black and white. Does Lasix improve performance or not? And what of horses who did not suffer from EIPH and were treated with Lasix? Did they run faster, too?

The Jockey Club decided to find out. In July, 1988, the Jockey Club commissioned Soma and his colleagues at the University of Pennsylvania's New Bolton Center to find definitive answers about Lasix at a cost of approximately $100,000.

Those answers could determine horseracing's medication policy forever.

Chapter 12

The Pennsylvania Study

The study that many hoped would finally end the debate over Lasix's performance-enhancing abilities was a cooperative effort between the New Bolton Center at the University of Pennsylvania's School of Veterinary Medicine, the management of Philadelphia Park, the Horsemen's Benevolent and Protective Association and the Pennsylvania Horse Racing Commission. Approval was needed from the Racing Commission to allow non-bleeders to be treated with Lasix.

The study, which lasted from July 13, 1988, through Feb. 1, 1989, was conducted by Dr. Larry Soma, Dr. Corinne Sweeney, Dr. Abby D. Maxson, Joseph Thompson, Susan Holcombe and Pamela Spencer.[1]

All trainers with horses not on the bleeders list, and therefore not receiving Lasix, at Philadelphia Park were invited to participate in the study, which consisted of three races. Eligible horses were examined for exercise-induced pulmonary hemorrhaging (EIPH) by a fiberoptic endoscope between 45 minutes and an hour and 15 minutes after running their first race (Race 1). The endoscope was advanced into the trachea to its full length or until blood was observed. The presence of hemorrhage was recorded, and horses were then categorized as either

---

[1] Sweeney, Corinne Raphel, Lawrence R. Soma, Abby D. Maxson, Joseph E. Thompson, Susan J. Holcombe and Pamela A. Spencer, "Effects of Furosemide on the Racing Times of Thoroughbreds," *American Journal of Veterinary Research*, Vol. 51, No. 5, May, 1990

EIPH-positive or EIPH-negative.

EIPH-negative horses were given 250 milligrams of furosemide four hours before their second race (Race 2) in accordance with the Lasix rules in Pennsylvania. All horses given Lasix were secured in their stall under supervision. Trainers withheld or provided hay and water during the detainment according to their usual procedure. Other medication was not knowingly given to any of the horses, and daily medication lists maintained by the state veterinarian were examined to determine non-steroidal, anti-inflammatory drug usage.

All EIPH-negative horses given Lasix before Race 2 were designated in the track program with an explanation to the public. "Full public disclosure of any horse given furosemide before racing was essential to maintain the integrity of the wagering process," the study said.

Imagine that: full public disclosure. Unfortunately, that constraint prevented the use of a placebo in a control group.

After Race 2, another endoscopic examination was done. If the horse remained EIPH-negative, he was examined again after the third race (Race 3). Furosemide was not given before Race 3. To be certified for the duration of the study as EIPH-negative, the horse had to show no evidence of EIPH after all three races and show no physical change that would impair racing performance during the study period, as determined by the trainer, state veterinarian and the project veterinarian.

EIPH-positive horses after Race 1 were re-examined by endoscope in the presence of a Pennsylvania State Racing Commission veterinarian to qualify for the bleeder's list. Four hours before Race 2, those horses were administered furosemide, ranging from 150 to 400 milligrams. Horses were examined again after Race 2. To remain in the study, a horse had to show no evidence of physical change as determined by the trainer, state veterinarian and project veterinarian that would impair the horse's racing performance through the rest of the study period.

There were 665 horses from 241 trainers in the study who completed Race 1. After Race 1, 329 horses (49.5 percent) were deemed EIPH-negative and 336 (50.5 percent) EIPH-positive.

A total of 235 of the 329 EIPH-negative horses completed Race 2 after being administered Lasix. (There were 94 EIPH-negative horses who did not race twice more before the meet ended, Feb. 1, 1989, and thus were not included in the study.) Of the 235, 173 horses (73.6 percent) remained EIPH-negative and 62 horses (26.4 percent) were EIPH-positive.

There were 139 of the remaining 173 horses who completed Race 3 (19 horses were withdrawn from the study upon request by their trainers, and 15 horses who were injured or eased during their race and were dropped from the study). Of the 139, 79 (56.8 percent) remained EIPH-negative. Sixty (43.2 percent) did not.

Of the 336 horses who were EIPH-positive after Race 1, 52 horses completed Race 2, without showing hemorrhaging. (There were 282 of the 336 who did not race again before the meet ended. Two others were eased and dropped from the study). Thirty-two of the 52 (61.5 percent) were still EIPH-positive after Race 2 and 20 (38.5 percent) were EIPH-negative.

Thus the final numbers for the horses who completed the study were 79 EIPH-negative horses and 52 EIPH-positives.

Race times of those 131 horses were adjusted to one-mile equivalent race times by two speed handicapping methods. Additionally, an analysis of covariance was used to adjust actual race times by the distance and the winning time of each race.

"All three methods of determining racing time indicated that geldings without EIPH had significantly faster race times when given furosemide before racing than when furosemide was not given before racing," the study said. "Females and colts without EIPH were determined to have faster racing times when furosemide was given before racing, but the difference was not significant. Geldings with EIPH had significantly faster race times when given furosemide before racing as determined by one of the speed handicapping method. There was a strong correlation between the one-mile equivalent race times as determined by the two speed handicapping methods for horses with and without EIPH."

The study concluded, "Furosemide failed to prevent the development of EIPH in many horses that were previously considered to be EIPH-negative. When given furosemide, 62 of 235 EIPH-negative horses (25.3 percent) were EIPH-positive after racing. Furosemide had questionable efficacy for prevention of EIPH in known EIPH-positive horses. Thirty-two of the 52 EIPH-positive horses (61.5 percent) given furosemide before a race remained EIPH-positive after that race."

Soma and Sweeney presented their findings at a press conference on May 9, 1990, and Jockey Club Chairman Dinny Phipps said he would share the findings of their study with all racing jurisdictions in North America.

"The Jockey Club is not a regulatory agency," Phipps said at the time. "But we wanted to increase our knowledge. The Jockey Club is against any artificial substance that enhances the racing ability of Thoroughbreds. From what we've seen today, furosemide enhances racing ability."

So what happened next?

Tony Chamblin, then executive vice president of the Association of Racing Commissioners International, told the *Daily Racing Form* in its two-day, extensive follow-up on the study's findings, "Unless scientific evidence is forthcoming to discredit these recent findings, racing commissions in jurisdictions which currently permit Lasix likely will be evaluating their rules in the near future."

New York, of course, didn't have to, as one of four states with Thoroughbred racing which banned Lasix on race-day (Idaho, South Dakota and Texas were the others.) "New York State has stood alone in its position in the use of Lasix," Richard Corbisiero, Jr., chairman of the New York State Racing and Wagering Board, said in the *Daily Racing Form* story. "We wish to congratulate our scientists at Cornell University, who, early on and at the risk of great criticism, advised us to ban this drug 48 hours prior to race time. We are gratified that New York's position on the use of Lasix has been vindicated."

It was short-lived.

Much of the reaction to the study outside New York was incredulous and/or fixed on preserving the status quo.

"Prohibiting Lasix would be a complete disaster," Greg Sanders, vice president of the Florida Division of the Horsemen's Benevolent and Protective Association, told the *Form*. "I believe that any movement to deny its use would result in a universal outcry from owners and trainers. If we treated horses with half of the medications used by other athletes, the Humane Society would scream."

Thomas Sweeney, Louisiana Downs executive vice president-general manager, said, "I still think it (Lasix) does help (control bleeding) and it does keep horses racing. It doesn't improve their performance. It simply keeps them on their level of performance."

Lyle Robey, chairman of the Kentucky State Racing Commission, said, "We've been using Lasix for a long time in Kentucky and one report I read said it made a horse run faster, and I don't believe that."

But Warren Wolf, racing secretary at River Downs, said Lasix is over-used: "Sometimes it is used when it's not necessary. I think it helps those horses that need it. However, some horses that do bleed should be given some time off for a rest."

Trainer Carl Nafzger said, "The whole economics of racing depends on Lasix. We must have it. New York doesn't have it. That is fine. They are trying to set an example for all of racing and I can appreciate that. But remember, you can race a horse in New York and if he bleeds, you can take him over to New Jersey, or to Pennsylvania or one of the other nearby medication states. In this respect, no Lasix doesn't hurt New York, and they can still be the role model.

"But, in general, racing can't survive without it. There are not enough sound horses to go around now and if you take away the bleeders, the racing secretaries can't fill the races."

Trainer Bob Holthus, who raced at Louisiana Downs and Oaklawn Park, reached the same conclusion about Lasix: "I think it definitely helps a horse run because it takes a lot of fluid out of their system and makes them lighter. I think without Lasix we would not be able to race in states like Louisiana, where it's hot. In fact, I doubt if you could get a very good card anywhere in the United States without Lasix."

You could in New York until 1995. That changed, too.

Just two and a half months after the study was released, the American Association of Equine Practitioners (AAEP) went on the record. In a statement which also called for a uniform medication policy — the exact same plea at the AAEP's Racetrack Medication Summit in Arizona, Dec. 4, 2002 — the AAEP stated, "In light of the current knowledge, AAEP will continue to maintain its position on medication in the racehorse. Our recommendation for the use of furosemide is that it be administered at a dosage of 250 mg. intravenously four hours prior to post time for the individual. A bleeder is a horse which demonstrates visible external evidence of exercise-induced pulmonary hemorrhage in the trachea, post-exercise, upon endoscopic examination. Such examination is to be performed by or in the presence of a regulatory veterinarian."

Twelve years later, Thoroughbred trainers in Kentucky could get their horses approved for Lasix by simply asking for it.

Another AAEP official, Dr. Gary Lavin, chairman of the AAEP racing committee, had a difficult time with the concept of Lasix enhancing performance. "It is mind-boggling," he told Mike Marten, who did a two-part series on Lasix for the *Daily Racing Form*, Aug. 10-11, 1990. "My mouth dropped open when I first heard the term in connection with Lasix. Keep in mind that Lasix has been used by humans for a long time, (so long) that most of our grandmothers are taking Lasix. But I don't see all the geriatrics out jumping fences. Of course Lasix allows horses to run faster. That's why we give them Lasix. But does that mean better than they ever ran before or just back to their level of performance when they were healthy?"

How would anyone know with first-time starters who begin their careers on Lasix?

In Marten's story, Dr. Corrine Sweeney said, "I wouldn't use the term performance-enhancing. Our study simply refers to increases and decreases in time. To use the word 'enhancing' suggests you know what that time was supposed to be. I can't tell you what God was supposed to make him do in that race. People on both sides have taken things out of context, gleaning what they want from the study."

Dr. John Pascoe, who pioneered bleeder studies in North America in the 1970s by using the fiberoptic endoscope, had no problem with the 1990 study questioning Lasix's efficacy in treating bleeders. "I find it amusing, given the number of times it's been said over the last 10 years, that so many people react so strongly to this latest statement," he told Marten. "My studies indicated Lasix did not appear to stop bleeding in most horses, but it did appear to reduce the amount of blood in the airways. This (Pennsylvania) report doesn't say that Lasix works. The basic issue is where you draw the line."

Corbisiero, the Chairman of the New York State Racing and Wagering Board, wanted more lines drawn. He proposed a gradual ban of Lasix throughout the country beginning with graded stakes that year (1990), then two-year-olds in 1991 and so on. Lasix would be banned nationally 48 hours before race time by 1993.

Phipps was more to the point in Marten's story: "Lasix should be illegal, the same as cocaine and other drugs that can influence the outcome of races. There are some questions remaining, but unanswered questions should not be used as an excuse to avoid action. Regulatory bodies have an immediate responsibility to re-examine their rules."

Others in the racing industry were infuriated with the study. "I wish the press and the politicians would quit shooting from the hip when it affects people's livelihood," Mike Steele, the national president of HBPA, told Marten. "I think I've read everything there is, and I've talked to quite a few experts, and now I'm ready to state publicly that the validity of the (Pennsylvania) study should be thrown out."

Trainer John Gosden, who had relocated his stable from Southern California to England, had a unique viewpoint having trained on both sides of the Atlantic Ocean. He shared his view with Marten: "My attitude is that under the conditions of American racing, particularly when you are in a city where the air quality is not good, where you have lung infections coupled with the stress of year-round racing, in that context, Lasix, when used intelligently, can be of great positive benefit. In England, we don't have the demanding training conditions that exist in America nor the poor air quality, so Lasix would be of no benefit."

Trainer Eddie Gaudet told Marten he was sure of Lasix's benefit in America: "Don't tell me it doesn't work. Until they come up with a permanent solution, there's nothing better. We can't all be fools except in New York."

Marjorie Everett, the chief executive officer of Hollywood Park, agreed: "Everybody can't be wrong except for a small group."

Today, the United States, Canada and Mexico comprised a small group — the only countries in the Northern Hemisphere, allowing Lasix, on race-day.

Chapter 13

New York: The Final Frontier

In 1987, New York trainer Howie Tesher had a star in his barn, Bolshoi Boy. The winner of the Illinois Derby in 1986, Bolshoi Boy won the Grade 2 Razorback Handicap at Oaklawn Park and the Budweiser Breeders' Cup Handicap at Gulfstream Park as a four-year-old in 1987. Bolshoi Boy was stabled and trained at Belmont Park, but Tesher was reluctant to race him in New York, even though Bolshoi Boy did on several occasions. Bolshoi Boy was a bleeder.

"My feeling on this is that it is another burden for the owners," Tesher told Mike Watchmaker of the *Daily Racing Form*, June 8, 1987, just two days after Bet Twice denied Alysheba the Triple Crown by winning the Belmont Stakes. "I'm here in New York, and I'd love to run Bolshoi Boy here, but what can I do?

"The rule on furosemide here also penalizes the fans, not just because Bolshoi Boy won't run here now, but because of horses like Demons Begone, who bled in the Derby. In the case of Alysheba, I don't think he needed furosemide, but why put that doubt in the minds of the 50,000 to 60,000 fans here who were betting?

"If I run Bolshoi Boy here in New York then send him to Maryland for a race, he must re-establish himself as a bleeder before he can get furosemide again. If I took him to New Jersey, that's okay, but not Maryland. There are no uniform rules on this problem, and that jeopardizes my horse."

Later in Watchmaker's story, Tesher acknowledged what had been obvious to handicappers since Lasix first came into vogue: "I think people realize that horses who run on furosemide for the first time tend to run big in a similar way to horses who run better with blinkers on for the first time."

Yet the *Daily Racing Form* would not include Lasix and bute information in horses' past performance lines for another three years.

Is there anyone in the world of racing naive enough to think that there weren't at least some people, be they owners or trainers or jockeys, betting on horses getting first time Lasix before it became public information?

Until September 1, 1995, that could not happen in New York. And some people were not only comfortable with New York's rule denying all medications 48 hours before a race, but were proud of that position.

"There are people who do anything to win and I don't think that's correct," said retired New York trainer Elliott Burch, who not only followed his father and grandfather into the business, but into the Hall of Fame as well. "I think a horse should race on hay and oats and vitamins. If they have a problem, lay them up so the problem is taken care of. Don't patch them up with drugs. I never used Lasix. Nor Butazolidin. I just don't believe in it. I know what effect it has. It flushes out a horse's system. You talk to any doctor. He'll tell you what it does."

Burch disagrees with the notion that horsemen who do not use Lasix on bleeders are being cruel. "That's bullshit," Burch said. "The main thing a trainer should do with a horse is to keep him sound and in good physical condition. They wouldn't do that with their own kids. I had just as much success as others without giving them stuff. Knock on wood, I never had a positive test in my career. My father didn't and I'm sure my grandfather didn't."

Another Hall of Fame trainer, John Nerud, was behind a 1999 proposal by the New York Thoroughbred Breeders, Inc., calling for all racing jurisdictions in the country to ban all medication 72 hours before race time. "That's when you enter the horse; that's when you stop treating him," said Nerud, who was then vice-president of the NYTB. "Any time you see a horse with first-time Lasix, he gets a lot of money. People think he's going to run and he does. It bothers me when I see a 10-horse field and nine of them are on Lasix. They aren't all nine bleeders."

Nerud, as well as the NYTB, did not expect other racing jurisdictions to suddenly sign on and abandon their medication policies allowing Lasix overnight. "At least I'm going to start people thinking," Nerud said at the time. "I don't think the trainers will resist this as much as the veterinarians and the racing commissions."

New York State's Racing and Wagering Board had been resisting peer pressure from other states for some 15 years with its 48-hour rule banning Lasix, as well as other drugs, when momentum for changing that policy began building in 1995 on the debatable premise that New York's fields were declining, and that banning Lasix could have an impact on the Breeders' Cup. The New York Racing Association, which had hosted the second Breeders' Cup at Aqueduct in 1985, and the seventh Breeders' Cup at Belmont Park in 1990, would again host the Cup at Belmont Park on Oct. 28, 1995.

But if the rationale for allowing Lasix in New York in 1995 was to accommodate the bleeders who would otherwise skip the Breeders' Cup, it was not based on fact.

In 1985, 82 horses competed in the Breeders' Cup at Aqueduct, the second highest total of the first six Breeders' Cups (the highest was 85 in the 1987 Cup at Hollywood Park). The 1990 Breeders' Cup at Belmont Park attracted 83 horses, three more than the previous year at Gulfstream Park.

Ironically, in the 1995 Breeders' Cup at Belmont Park with Lasix, 80 horses competed, a total lower than the previous two times racing's championship day visited New York.

But there was more than the upcoming Breeders' Cup which brought Lasix to the bargaining table in 1995.

When Kenny Noe signed on as the new president of the New York Racing Association in late October, 1994, he told Matt Graves of the *Albany Times-Union* one of his priorities was medication. "I'd be open to discussions about uniform rules of medication," Noe said.

At the time, there was a uniform rule about one medication, Lasix, in every racing state except New York. Every other jurisdiction had it, and New York's horsemen saw a potential ally in Noe, who has always been horsemen-friendly.

If Lasix advocates in New York needed another teammate, they found one in Dr. Jerry Bilinski, a veterinarian and Thoroughbred owner and breeder, who served as the Chairman of the New York State Racing and Wagering Board from May 2, 1995 through Aug. 29, 1996.

Under Bilinski's leadership, the New York State Racing and Wagering Board took on the Lasix issue. "It was already on the burner before I got involved," said Bilinski, who was replaced as Board Chairman by Michael Hoblock. "It got brought up that there were certain portions of the industry that were concerned about it. Lasix was an economic decision. Triple Crown horses wouldn't race in the Belmont Stakes. That hurt us economically."

That exact sentiment had been expressed to Bilinski's predecessor as chairman of the Racing and Wagering Board, Richard Corbisiero, Jr., In a letter to Corbisiero dated December 27, 1994 — accompanying a signed petition from his association — Doug Warren of the Standardbred Owners Association, Inc., of New York, asked for the "controlled use" of not only Lasix, but Bute, as well.

"We know that horsemen throughout the state, including those in Thoroughbred racing, are desirous of changing the State's laws regarding this matter," the letter said. "The hard reality is that these products are permitted in many other states (including New

106

Jersey), and the restriction in New York both reduces the quantity and quality of racing here. It also imposes an economic hardship on New York trainers. Many owners are obligated to stable their horses that race with Lasix to (sic) New Jersey (or other states) since they can not compete at Yonkers Raceway, or any New York track."

Another plea to allow Lasix came two and a half months later from the New York Horsemen's Benevolent and Protective Association. In a letter to the New York State Racing and Wagering Board Chief Counsel, New York HBPA President Al Fried, Jr., wrote: "To be able to compete with other racing jurisdictions for this ever decreasing horse population, we must adopt a race day therapeutic medication program that allows the use of furosemide, generally known as Lasix."

The message got through to Bilinski. "The main point, at that time, was that if it hurt us economically, we should look at it, unless there were negative reasons not to," Bilinski said.

Seven years later, Bilinski wonders if he had done the right thing. "In hindsight, looking at Lasix, I had the naive assumption that people would abide by the rules and use the medication as prescribed," Bilinski said in 2002. "Obviously, if you looked at every veterinary bill, would you see that all the horses on Lasix showed endoscopes? I've been told it's 50 percent."

Terry Meyocks, Kenny Noe's protege who succeeded him as NYRA's president, has also revisited his position on Lasix. "I was always a believer in Lasix over the years, but I've kind of changed my mind," he said in 2002. "Until they get the testing down, the integrity issue is important."

In 1995, it was not important enough.

On May 18, 1995, the New York State Racing and Wagering Board held an "information session" in New York City about changing the 48-hour rule to allow Lasix at New York State's Thoroughbred and harness tracks. "All participants said they favored the change," a New York State Racing and Wagering Board press release said on May 25.

In that press release, the Board announced its unanimous approval to publish a draft rule to allow the use of furosemide beginning September 1, 1995, opening day at Belmont Park's fall meet.

"There have been a number of clinical trials that show about 85 percent of horses that race bleed; therefore I fully expect that a large number of horses currently racing in New York will be put on Lasix once it is allowed," Bilinski said in the press release. "This shouldn't be a surprise if it happens. Furthermore, we hope that the rule change instituting the controlled administration of furosemide will provide a more level playing field and help attract quality horses that otherwise might not race here."

As with any rule change of state law in New York State, the proposed change is published in the New York State Register and allows for a 45-day public comment period before implementation.

A lot of people had something to say about reversing New York State's stand on Lasix, including a former Racing and Wagering Board member, Joe O'Dea, and former Racing and Wagering Board Chairman John Van Lindt.

In a July 8, 1995, letter to the Board, O'Dea pleaded that the Board allow Lasix in a trial run first: "For the good of racing and the Board, I would suggest that the proposed Lasix rule be implemented for an advertised trial period (6 months or a year) and careful records kept to determine the effects of the Rule on the percentage of winning favorites, the number of breakdowns and sudden death syndrome, post-race positives for other substances, attrition rate in horses, influence on the entry box, etc. We should make this an objective endeavor, not just as it appears a 'me too move' to pander to the misdirected political penchant for uniformity.

"I think you know that I'll do my best in the interest of racing. Let's get it right before implementation. New York is a leader, not a follower. The OTB (Off-Track Betting) idea was implemented without sufficient prior thought and it had been a plague on New York since."

O'Dea's letter followed a letter 10 days earlier to Racing and Wagering Board Member Ben Liebman from Van Lindt, who had moved on to become executive vice president and general manager of Hialeah. Van Lindt wrote, "It has never been the policy in New York to ban the use of any approved medication. The policy was not to allow any medication to be administered that could conceivably alter the outcome of a pari-mutuel horse race. In essence, two philosophies were considered. The first was that all the horses came out of the gate evenly matched. No one had a medication advantage. The second was that no animal be given a medication which could possibly endanger its well-being.

"Those of us who were privileged to administer the laws and rules of pari-mutuel wagering in New York were consistently warned that furosemide, besides being a medication to control bleeding, also acted to enhance the racing performance of the Thoroughbred, and that, as a diuretic, could mask the presence of other more insidious medications."

The letter went on, "You are being told that the current proposal that is being considered will increase the available horse population at New York tracks. In my present capacity, I am quite familiar with the problems faced by the owners and trainers and all of the people connected with putting on the Thoroughbred horse racing show. Most of them are wonderful people, hardworking and dedicated to the animals that they seek to bring to the races. I can certainly sympathize with their day-to-day struggles. As a racetrack executive, I can also sympathize with the New York Racing Association's desire to have more horses available to compete. However, again, how do these aspects of racetrack life overcome the two philosophies upon which New York's no medication policy is based?

"New York has never, as several have suggested, buried its head in the sand on the medication issue. But being alone does not mean being wrong. Far from being 'behind the times,' I have always believed that the widespread and often indiscriminate use of medication has the capacity of debasing this magnificent sport. Comparisons with other 'big league sports' are obvious. But, at least, there, the participant can make a cognizant, if often irrational decision on the use of a drug to enhance his or her performance or alleviate the pain associated with it. As a backstretch employee once told me, horses are very trusting animals. They put their trust in us to care and protect them. That is a very awesome responsibility ...

"I would urge you not to disturb a sound and rational medication policy that I, for one, was proud to have once helped to implement."

Another letter to the Board, from Abram Jack Cuttler of Schenectady, raised another issue: "Is not a 'bleeder' an inferior horse, and should we not be trying to improve the breed here and get rid of the 'bleeders?' Instead of improving the breed, your rule is going to perpetuate a serious weakness in horses.

"Also, I think this is the camel's nose under the tent. Next thing you know, you will legalize bute and God knows what else. These drugs mask other drugs and how do you deal with that? It was always some satisfaction to me that the New York tracks kept drugs out of the doping out (handicapping) I have done with the Racing Form. I think your proposal would turn Saratoga into an Arkansas dog track!"

The pleas to preserve the no-medication rule in New York were drowned by a tidal wave of support for Lasix from horsemen.

On September 1, 1995, New York became just another racing state allowing race-day use of Lasix.

And Lasix did have a positive impact of reducing the number of incidents of epistaxis, horses bleeding from the nostrils. In three years before 1995, there were 59, 57 and 58 incidents, respectively. In 1995, there were 25 before the rule change September 1, and just four the rest of the year. In the ensuing years, there were nine, 13, 16, 12, 12 and just eight in 2001.

"It seems to help," said Dr. Neil Clearly, the New York Racing Association's Chief Examining Veterinarian. "It seems to mitigate it. Those numbers reflect that."

There are other numbers reflecting how New York is rapidly slipping into Lasix-dependency like every other racing state in America.

In 1996, 12,989 of 19,857 starters (65.4 percent) were on Lasix in New York. In 2001, 16,200 of 18,927 (85.6 percent) raced on Lasix.

In 1996, 1,622 winners of 2,392 New York races (67.8 percent) were on Lasix. In 2001, 2,090 of 2,368 New York race winners (88.3 percent) were on Lasix.

"It's greatly over-used, and I think that the literature and the research that has been done on Lasix raises more questions than answers," said Dr. Ted Hill, a former veterinarian who is the New York Racing Association Jockey Club Steward. "You question how much benefit you get from Lasix. Having been on the other side (as a veterinarian), I've seen it help horses, not all of them. When you're looking at upwards of 75 to 80 percent of all horses racing on Lasix, in my mind, I can't believe it's clinically justified. There is evidence that it does decrease the severity of at least some individuals. A lot of the research is contradictory."

Hill, who has been working at NYRA since 1977, brought up another salient point.

"Prior to September, 1995, when we allowed Lasix, we raced a lot of good horses in a lot of good races," Hill said. "If bleeding was such a big problem, what happened? I don't think we had poor racing. How did we get by all those years without Lasix?

"Lasix is not totally innocuous, even though it's used in such enormous quantities. Some horses react severely to it. Some horses become very quiet, too quiet. Horses can get a colic or a spastic gut. It's not hard for our horses in extensive training and stall environments to get uncomfortable. Some horses run very poorly on Lasix. I'd like to see that it's not in blanket usage in New York."

Hill does not buy into the "No Lasix equals cruelty" argument. "I guess I've heard that," he said. "I don't know if those people have taken the time to read the science before they would make a statement like that. I have more problems with the whip than I would of depriving a horse Lasix as being inhumane. I don't think there's any science to justify that at all. Horses are individuals. I think those cases have to be taken on an individual by individual basis."

Instead, just about every Thoroughbred in the United States and Canada is treated the same: Lasix whether they need it or not; Lasix whether it masks other drugs or not; Lasix whether it alters performance or not.

But in the bigger picture of global Thoroughbred racing, the United States and Canada stand virtually alone on race-day Lasix. "I don't think the literature today supports that we're the only countries that have it right," Hill said. "I can't say that we've got it right."

New York By The Numbers

Cases of Epistaxis

1992-59

1993-57

1994-58

1995-29 (25 before Sept. 1)

1996-9

1997-13

1998-16

1999-12

2000-12

2001-8

Starters and Winners on Lasix in New York

Year	Starters	Starters on Lasix	Pct.	Races	Winners on Lasix	Pct.
1996	19,857	12,989	65.4	2,392	1,622	67.8
1997	19,749	14,073	71.2	2,431	1,783	73.3
1998	19,111	14,594	76.4	2,370	1,907	80.5
1999	19,193	15,554	81.0	2,368	1,984	83.8
2000	19,485	16,354	83.9	2,369	2,043	86.2
2001	18,927	16,200	85.6	2,368	2,090	88.3

Chapter 14

Into Africa?

At a July, 1998, Members' Information Meeting of the Jockey Club of Southern Africa, the legendary golfer Gary Player, an avid Thoroughbred owner and breeder, proposed that the Jockey Club permit the use of furosemide. Player owns a 12,500-acre ranch in South Africa, midway between Cape Town and Johannesburg.

"In support of his proposal, Mr. Player cited the state of New York which had recently (sic) decided to permit the administration of Lasix to horses running in races within its jurisdiction," reported the *Racing Review*, the newsletter of the Jockey Club of Southern Africa, in an article written by Tony Barnes entitled "The Lasix Lowdown," in its January-February, 2000 issue. "He strongly urged The Jockey Club to obtain first hand information on the New York decision."

The Jockey Club did.

South Africa was a founding member of the International Federation of Horseracing Authorities, and had signed that body's International Agreement with dozens of other countries. "All of the leading racing countries in the world, excluding those in the Americas, have committed themselves to the provisions of the recently revised Article Six, in that they essentially prohibit the use of any substance in a horse during a race which could give a horse an advantage or a disadvantage in that race," the *Racing Review* article stated.

Allowing Lasix would require the Jockey Club to change

South Africa's race-day medication policy, and then decide that Lasix was a desirable medication to allow.

In the *Racing Review* article, the Jockey Club outlined its medication philosophy, which states, "that if a horse requires treatment/medication, it should be treated/medicated by a suitably qualified person (normally a Veterinary Surgeon) and allowed to rest until the treatment/medication has had the desired effect and the medication is out of the horse's system."

The article explained the rationale behind that philosophy:

• The horse has no say in the treatment/medication administered to him.

• The horse's participation in the race could aggravate the condition for which it was given medication.

• The horse will, because of the medication, be at an advantage or a disadvantage compared to the other horses in his race.

• Medicating a horse has the potential for abuse of the horse, giving an unfair advantage to his connections and providing an unfair disadvantage for punters (bettors).

Regarding the contention that Lasix allows a horse to race to his potential, the article states, "If a horse can only 'achieve its potential' while under medication, surely this means that one needs artificial means to obtain the desired result. Then, at what point does 'achieving its potential' become unacceptable? Does the use of a steroid, for example, enable a horse to develop to its potential?"

The article then confronts topics which are too seldom addressed by Lasix advocates.

Under "The Image of Racing," the article said, "Regrettably, racing does not enjoy a good image as a sport. This makes it difficult for racing to compete with other sports for sponsorships and with other forms of gaming for customers. If racing is seen to allow horses to be given medication to enable them to participate in a race, this will inevitably harm racing's image. It is likely to be characterized both as a cruel sport and as a sport and/or form of gaming where results can be changed through the use of medication."

Under "The International View," the article continued: "All of the world's leading racing jurisdictions outside the Americas believe, and recently confirmed, that the presence of medication in racehorses during races is undesirable and must be prohibited. There is, to date, no new or compelling evidence which suggests that the countries which have adopted this philosophy are wrong or that they need to again review their collective viewpoint."

Under "The Implications of Permitting Medication in Racing," the article quotes Andy Beyer's column in the *Washington Post* after the Kentucky Racing Commission changed its rules regarding the bronchodilator clenbuterol:

"Naive outsiders might expect that the racing industry would try to rid itself of clenbuterol. But the industry traditionally moves in the opposite direction — it stops cheating by legalizing a banned substance. It did that with both Butazolidin and Lasix. And this week, the Kentucky Racing Commission liberalized its rules governing the use of clenbuterol.

"It is easy to react cynically whenever a veterinarian, trainer or spokesman for a horsemen's organization utters the word 'therapeutic' — particularly after the campaigns to get Bute and Lasix legalized in the 1970s. The first trainers to use Lasix illegally were able to bring about stunning form reversals: sometimes they would claim a horse and improve him overnight by as much as 10 or 20 lengths by administering the diuretic. Eventually, most trainers were clamoring to use the wondrous drug. So horsemen and veterinarians went before state racing commissions and assured them that Lasix was a therapeutic medication that doesn't affect horses' form. Of course, everybody who had witnessed those 10 and 20-length form reversals knew this was poppycock, but even today horsemen and vets maintain this fiction. And now, here we go again.

"Every other major racing nation forbids the presence of the

117

drugs in a horse's system on race day, and the sport manages to survive well enough without them in England, France, Australia and Japan. But since America abandoned the traditional standard of 'hay, oats and water,' the quality of this country's Thoroughbreds has steadily declined."

On August 14, 1998, a meeting of the National Federation of Owners and Trainers met in South Africa to discuss pre-race medication. A representative of Gary Player pushed for the permission of Lasix in South Africa. Although an overwhelming majority of those present were against the use of Lasix, the Lasix proponents continued with their request, and a meeting between South African racing officials and a cross-section of horsemen and officials from Kentucky and New York was conducted in December, 1998.

Some two months later, Dr. Kenneth Hinchcliff of Ohio State, who has published several studies of Lasix, spoke to the Equine Practitioners Group (EPG) of the South African Veterinary Association and then to a group from the National Federation of Owners and Trainers which included owners, trainers and veterinary surgeons, members of the Jockey Club management team and some of its veterinary surgeons.

"My job was informational," Hinchcliff said in April, 2002. "I didn't try to influence their decision. I don't have an opinion on whether Lasix should be used or not. People say, 'Hinchcliff says this' or 'Hinchcliff says that.' I try to be strictly neutral. I've caught flack from both sides over the years."

South Africa's racing officials saw no reason to change its policy of not allowing race-day medication to permit the use of Lasix.

"The conclusion of the EPG and those who attended the meeting mentioned above was that there was no justification for the administration of Lasix to horses participating in Southern African racing," the *Racing Review* reported.

A subsequent visit to the United States "did not reveal any

new veterinary or research data which had emerged to make the authorities in New York State change their stance on the use of Lasix. The evidence at our disposal suggests that if the decision was influenced by any factor other than to conform with the mainstream, it was influenced by financial considerations. New York racing has apparently been finding it difficult to fill its fields and indications are that owners and trainers from other states were not keen to race their horses in New York."

The conclusion of the *Racing Review* article? "The issue of medication in racing has generated negative perceptions for racing and is rejected by all leading racing jurisdictions outside the Americas. It should be recognized that once this principle is sacrificed, the likely consequence is a proliferation of permissible drugs.

"While the use of Lasix has been accepted in Thoroughbred racing in the Americas, its use must be regarded as questionable. It is being used to treat a veterinary problem, EIPH ... The evidence which has been gained from this investigation suggests that there can be no moral or veterinary justification for permitting the use of Lasix in Southern African racing."

Chapter 15

The Rest of the World

On the other side of the world from the United States, racing officials in Dubai of the United Arab Emirates wanted their own day of world-caliber championship racing and initiated the Dubai World Cup in 1996.

In its seventh year, March 23, 2002, the Dubai World Cup had grown to five races. A total of 69 Thoroughbreds entered the United Arab Emirates Derby, Dubai Sheema Classic, Dubai Golden Shaheen, the Dubai Duty Free and the Dubai World Cup. The first four races each carried a purse of $2 million. The Dubai World Cup was worth $6 million.

There is no wagering in the country of Dubai.

And, as in almost every other foreign racing jurisdiction except in North and South America, there are no race-day drugs, including Lasix.

That did not stop American-based Cigar, Silver Charm and Captain Steve from winning the Dubai World Cup in 1996, 1998 and 2001, respectively, and it did not prevent eight American horses from competing in the 2002 Dubai World Cup races.

Five were in the Golden Shaheen Sprint: the brilliant 2001 champion three-year-old filly Xtra Heat, Caller One, Bonapaw, Echo Eddie and Men's Exclusive. All had been racing on Lasix. Caller One, Echo Eddie and Men's Exclusive had also been racing on Bute. Caller One won the Sprint by a head over Echo Eddie. Xtra Heat was third and Men's Exclusive fourth.

Del Mar Show and Val Royal, competing in the Dubai Duty Free, and Western Pride, contesting the Dubai World Cup, had also been racing on Lasix.

Some of the American horses' rivals in Dubai had competed in the $2.3 million Hong Kong Cup, the $545,000 Singapore Classic, the $1,389,000 February Stakes in Tokyo, the $1.47 million Prix de l'Arc de Triomphe in Paris and the $488,000 Queen Elizabeth II Stakes at Ascot. All without race-day Lasix.

But as telling as that is about Lasix-free championship racing around the world, what is even more striking is that American owners and trainers have been willing to send their best Lasix-using horses halfway around the globe to compete in rich championship races in Dubai without that crutch on race day. They all survived the experience of racing Lasix-free, and every year, new American, Lasix-using horses come to Dubai and race without it.

In fact, in every single racing country in the world except Saudi Arabia and seven nations in the Americas (the United States, Canada, Mexico, Argentina, Brazil, Chile and Venezuela), Lasix is not allowed.

There is almost an international consensus not only banning Lasix, but all drugs which can influence a horse's performance.

In 1961, horseracing authorities in the United States, France, Great Britain and Ireland began coordinating their efforts to protect the integrity of racing and improve the quality of the breed.

Six years later, they began an annual International Conference of racing countries around the globe. Annually, this conference, held in Paris, brings nations together to seek common ground and take action for the welfare of not only the racing horse but the sport of racing as well.

That cooperation ultimately led to the International Agreement on Breeding and Racing, which was first endorsed by racing nations at the International Conference in 1974, and is updated annually.

In 1993, the International Federation of Horseracing Authorities was formed and now numbers more than 60 members. Its main objectives include: coordinating and harmonizing the rules of member countries regarding breeding and racing; ensuring the quality and fairness of racing in the interest of both the breed and the public and protecting the welfare of horses, jockeys and the public.

Member nations can agree or disagree on any of the articles of the International Agreement.

Article Six of the International Agreement addresses prohibited substances. Its objective: "To protect the integrity of horseracing through controlling the use of substances capable of giving a horse an advantage or being disadvantaged in a race, contrary to the horse's inherent merits."

Much more than the use of Lasix is addressed in the sweeping provision of prohibited substances, item No. 10 of Article Six, which bans substances "capable at any time of acting on one or more of the following mammalian body systems:"

- The Nervous System
- The Cardiovascular System
- The Respiratory System
- The Digestive System
- The Urinary System
- The Reproductive System
- The Musculoskeletal System
- The Blood System
- The Immune System except for licensed vaccines
- The Endocrine System
- Endocrine secretions and their synthetic counterparts
- Masking agents.

Additionally, "A finding of a prohibited substance means a finding of the substance itself or a metabolite of the substance or an isomer of the substance or an isomer of a metabolite. The finding of any scientific indicator of administration or other exposure to a prohibited substance is also equivalent to the finding of the substance."

Article Six also addresses thresholds, sampling, sanctions including disqualifications, trainer's responsibilities, race-day regulations and laboratory services.

The following countries agreed to Article Six completely:

Algeria, Austria, Bahrain, Belgium, Chad, Cyprus, Czech Republic, Denmark, France, Germany, Great Britain, Greece, Hong Kong, Hungary, India, Ireland, Israel, Italy, Kenya, Korea, Lebanon, Mauritius, Morocco, Netherlands, Norway, Pakistan, Panama, Peru, Poland, Qatar, Rumania, Russia, Slovakia, Slovenia, South Africa, Spain, Sweden, Switzerland, Thailand, Tunisia, United Arab Emirates and Yugoslavia.

Additionally, Australia, Japan, Macao, Malaysia/Singapore and Turkey all back item No. 10, the one on prohibited substances, and most other items of Article Six with one or two exceptions. For example, Australia backs Article Six except the item on sanctions and a threshold limit of carbon dioxide. Japan endorses all of Article Six except a provision on chain of custody of samples and threshold limits.

The following countries agree with Article Six, including item No. 10, but allow furosemide: Argentina, Brazil, Chile, Mexico, Saudi Arabia and Venezuela.

Only one nation in the entire world disagrees with all of item No. 10, the very concept of prohibited substances. Go to the head of the class if you guessed it was the United States.

We stand alone.

Should the leaders of the racing industry in the United States take comfort that our pro-Lasix position is shared by Argentina, Brazil, Chile, Mexico, Saudi Arabia and Venezuela? Or that Canada chose not to agree with any part of Article Six?

John Gosden, who has trained Thoroughbreds on both sides of the Atlantic Ocean, in Southern California (from 1979 to 1989) and in England, sees good and bad in Lasix. "Most horses in their lifetime will use it," he said. "It is part of stressed athletic ability. I think that's a fact we can't escape. I will often work horses on Lasix. If it stops their bleeding, they maintain their self-confidence.

"I see Lasix as a drug that if used intelligently and rationally can be therapeutic. What I don't like to see is this blanket coverage. That's what happened in the States, and I think that's unfortunate. I think the racehorse we breed and race now is a more delicate creature than 25 or 30 years ago."

In the United States, that more delicate creature can race on Lasix. Almost everywhere else in the world, he can not. "I think the demands of racing in America are very different than in other parts of the world," Gosden said. "They're training on racetracks, breaking from the gate. In Europe, unless it's a sprint, the horses collect themselves. I think it's right not to have medication in Europe. I remained unconvinced that the bleeding problem here grows."

In a student dissertation for the Royal Agricultural College in Cirencester, Gloucestershire, England, Jessica Winkworth conducted a study to determine whether Lasix affects performance by comparing race times between British and American horses. Two hundred and twenty-seven horses in Group I, II and III stakes comprised the study over four distances: seven furlongs, one mile, a mile and a quarter and a mile and a half. She concluded, "It can be clearly identified when looking at the results that the American times are faster than the times made by the British horses whether it be a significant amount or not. This could be because the American horses ran on the drug Lasix, perhaps putting them at an advantage over the British horses, as the drug is not used in Britain. Another alternative explanation could be due to the Americans, for the most part, having faster courses that the British."

She also found when comparing British horses racing in America on Lasix against American horses on Lasix, that the American horses were faster, "although the differences were extremely small."

She found that British horses running on Lasix in America had faster times than British horses in America not on Lasix.

She wanted to do a statistical analysis between American horses running on and off Lasix, but could not do one. The reason? "A limited number of horses running off the drug."

At a website on the Internet called bridleup.com, an assistant trainer born in England, John Elliott, offered his take of Lasix in America and why horses using Lasix for the first time frequently run better: "I feel it has little to do with bleeding. If a horse was set to carry six or eight pounds less on his back, one would expect it to be able to go faster ... It is in every trainer's interest to get his horses onto Lasix. I personally have heard a vet ask in mid-scoping, 'You do want it to be a bleeder, don't you?' And no one but he can see up the scope, so every trainer needs a vet on his side. If a trainer runs one not on the drug, he probably wants someone to think there is improvement to be made in the hope someone might claim it.

"The whole system makes a mockery of American racing and leads to breeding from horses that are bleeders. I come from England where there is no Lasix. English racing is drug free and should be proud of it. Sadly, American racing is so entrenched in the drugged horses system, it is unlikely to ever change. But don't make the mistake of thinking the only reason Lasix is used to prevent bleeding. It's just to put your horse on a level playing field with all the others."

Chapter 16

Standard for Standardbreds?

In January, 1989, a stakes committee of the Hambletonian Society met and discussed several proposals regarding the Hambletonian Stakes for three-year-old trotters, harness racing's equivalent of the Kentucky Derby, and the Hambletonian Oaks, the accompanying stakes for three-year-old trotting fillies. Several recommendations were made and presented to the Hambletonian Society Board of Directors at a meeting the following month. One of the recommendations was to take a stand against Lasix and ban it from both the Hambletonian and Hambletonian Oaks beginning with the 1989 conditions of eligibility for the 1991 editions of both stakes.

Lasix-free stakes racing in America. Incredible.

That recommendation not only passed the Board of Directors, but was expanded to include Bute as well, and to encompass the elimination races for both stakes.

"It was received as in the best interest of the event," said Tom Charters, the president and CEO of the Hambletonian Society and Breeders Crown. "There didn't seem to be much discussion about it."

Accordingly, the conditions for the 1991 Hambletonian and Hambletonian Oaks were revised and to this day still read:

"No horse shall be permitted to race in the Open (Hambletonian) or the Oaks with Butazolidin or Lasix."

The only change in 13 years has been to affix Lasix's new

name, Salix, to the rule. From 1998 through 2001 alone, 81 three-year-old fillies and 83 three-year-old colts have raced Lasix-free in the eliminations and finals of the two stakes.

"The Hambletonian stands not only as the most important trotting race in the world, but one that sets an example in integrity," said Ebby Gerry, Jr., the first vice-president of the Hambletonian Society and President of the Harness Racing Museum and Hall of Fame. "The feeling was that the Hambletonian had to set the example as the cleanest, purest race. We wanted it completely clean. We decided we didn't want horses in the Hambletonian on medication."

Of course, not every harness horseman in America agreed. "We get flack from year to year," Gerry said. "Our attitude is, 'It's in the conditions when you enter the horse. If you don't like the conditions, don't enter the horse.'"

And that was it. Through early 2002, Charters reported there has not been a single lawsuit. "There were directors who owned horses who had been racing on Lasix and didn't use it in the Hambletonian," Charters said. "You can make an argument that Classic races are proving grounds for the breeding shed, as far as selection of horses."

This does not suggest that Lasix use in harness racing is inconsequential. While not as prevalent as in Thoroughbreds, Lasix use on Standardbreds is apparently on the rise, particularly on weekends when the richest races are contested.

Documenting that is difficult. Many charts of harness races, including those in the program at The Meadowlands every night, do not indicate whether or not a horse raced on Lasix. To check it out, bettors must either use the New York racing newspaper *Sports Eye*, which lists Lasix users in paragraph form underneath each chart, or go back to past programs and take notes.

While Lasix is not allowed in the Hambletonian or the Hambletonian Oaks, the use of Lasix in the Breeders Crown is minuscule compared to Thoroughbred racing's Breeders' Cup.

Regardless, the entire field of older pacers for the 2002 Presidential Pace, Jan. 26, raced on Lasix at The Meadowlands.

Fifteen nights later, the top seven-year-old trotter Magician used Lasix for the first time in a leg of the 2002 Su Mac Lad Series. The decision to use Lasix on this $2.7 million earner was not an easy one for his trainer, Earl Cruise. "I hated to put him on it, but I had to," Cruise said a month later. "I don't want to be in the middle of the summer and miss 10 days (because he bled) and miss a million-dollar race."

According to Cruise, Magician had bled sporadically earlier in his career. "He has bled on occasion, but I think it was isolated cases," Cruise said. "He made $2.7 million without Lasix. I didn't want to do it with him, because I knew it would be hard on his system. But if he's bleeding, he's got to have it."

Cruise said he has "mixed emotions" about Lasix. "You can look at a horse and see if he's on Lasix," he said. "They look a little gaunt. I hated to do it to this guy. I think a lot of trainers don't like putting them (their horses) on it. But some horsemen love it and put horses on it if they're not bleeding."

Magician's use of Lasix may have had repercussions. According to an April 1 story by Lars G. Palm, the European correspondent for *The Horseman and Fair World*, Magician was not invited to Europe's premier trotting race, the Elitlopp, May 26, because Sweden does not allow the use of race-day Lasix.

When another top trotter, first-time Lasix user Will Sykes, won the first division of the Father Foley Series at The Meadowlands, March 17, 2002, John Campbell, the sport's all-time leading driver, said, "He was certainly improved with the Lasix."

Stan Bergstein, executive vice-president of Harness Tracks of America and a columnist for the *Daily Racing Form*, likens Lasix usage in horse racing to his Blue Balloon Theory. A trainer ties a blue balloon to his horse's tail before a race. The horse wins. The next night, there are dozens of horses with blue balloons tied to their tails.

"I think that people use Lasix because other people use it," Bergstein said. "I think it's a herd instinct. I believe in my own mind that it's still a masking agent and in many cases is used as a masking agent. I think that's a downright disgrace."

Bob "Hollywood" Heyden, the press box manager and TV analyst of The Meadowlands, did a random nine-week survey of recent Lasix use by Standardbreds at the country's premier harness racing meet.

Heyden found that 34.8 percent of horses raced on Lasix in his 1996 sample; 39.7 percent in 1999 and 45.4 percent in 2002. That's not all he found.

"What I did was strictly informal," he said. "I took three random weeks in 1996, 1999 and 2002. They were spread out through the season, and the entire week was used. One thing is quite consistent. The weekend, when most of the older, established horses are competing, has almost double the amount of Lasix users as during the week, especially when the younger horses hit the track later in the season."

A closer look at racing at The Meadowlands in February and March, 2002, confirmed Heyden's hypothesis. The Saturday night percentage of Lasix users jump off the page.

Lasix at The Meadowlands

Night	Number	Percentage
Thursday, Feb. 7	33-109	30.3
Friday, Feb. 8	79-114	69.3
Saturday, Feb. 9	79-120	65.8
Wednesday, Feb. 13	32-96	33.3
Saturday, Feb. 16	83-120	69.2
Wednesday, Mar 6	39-134	29.1
Thursday, March 7	42-109	38.5
Saturday, March 9	80-108	74.1
Thursday, March 14	41-101	40.6
Friday, March 15	59-109	54.1
Saturday, March 16	93-123	75.6
Thursday, March 21	36-94	38.3
Friday, March 22	61-113	54.0
Saturday, March 23	83-121	68.6
Sunday, March 24	48-111	43.2
TOTALS	888-1,682	52.8

Would there be a similar pattern at other tracks?

In the week from Monday, Feb. 4 through Sunday, Feb. 10 at Woodbine in Toronto, the numbers also jumped up on that Saturday with 46 of 102 starters on Lasix. The night before, it was 32 of 100. The day after, 20 of 106.

The percentages also increased dramatically from Wednesday, Feb. 13, to Saturday, Feb. 16, at Dover Downs in Delaware, Freehold Raceway in New Jersey and Pompano Park in Florida.

At Dover, 50.5 percent used Lasix that Wednesday compared to 66.7 the following Saturday.

At Freehold, 45.2 percent used Lasix that Wednesday, while 62.5 percent used it the ensuing Saturday.

At Pompano Park, 44.7 percent raced on Lasix Wednesday, and 69.4 percent the following Saturday.

In a sample of six harness tracks open on Wednesday, Feb. 13, 2002 — Dover Downs, Freehold, Maywood, The Meadowlands, Monticello and Pompano Park — 44.36 percent used Lasix.

In a sample of 11 harness tracks racing Saturday, Feb. 16, 2002, Balmoral, Cal-Expo, Dover, Freehold, The Meadowlands, The Meadows, Northfield, Northville Downs, Pompano, Rosecroft and Yonkers, 61.81 percent used Lasix.

In a sample of 11 tracks open Friday, March 8, 2002 — Cal-Expo, Fraser Downs, Maywood, The Meadowlands, The Meadows, Northfield Park, Northville Downs, Pompano Park, Rosecroft, Woodbine and Yonkers — 56.8 percent used Lasix.

The numbers which are most startling are at Cal-Expo on a Saturday night. Apparently, not only are California Thoroughbreds using Lasix more frequently than any other state, but California Standardbreds are as well.

Why?

Of a total sample of 3,468 Standardbred starters, 1,854 (53.46 percent) were on Lasix.

Standardbreds on Lasix

Wednesday, Feb. 13, 2002

Track	Number	Percentage
Dover	52-103	50.5
Freehold	42-93	45.2
Maywood	37-82	45.1
Meadowlands	32-96	33.3
Monticello	42-89	47.2
Pompano	51-114	44.7
TOTALS	256-577	44.36

Saturday, Feb. 16, 2002

Track	Number	Percentage
Balmoral	84-113	74.3
Cal Expo	90-99	90.9
Dover	72-108	66.7
Freehold	65-104	62.5
Meadowlands	83-120	69.2
The Meadows	74-96	77.1
Northfield	94-112	83.9
Northville Dns	47-94	50.0
Pompano	77-111	69.4
Rosecroft	70-91	76.9
Yonkers	50-93	53.8
TOTALS	806-1,141	70.63

Friday, March 8, 2002

Track	Number	Percentage
Cal-Expo	63-89	70.8
Fraser Downs	16-53	30.2
Maywood	70-95	73.7
Meadowlands	70-103	68.0
The Meadows	83-109	76.1
Northfield Park	75-117	64.1
Northville Dns	51-94	54.3
Pompano Park	52-114	45.6
Rosecroft	56-90	62.2
Woodbine	27-100	27.0
Yonkers	35-89	39.3
TOTALS	598-1,053	56.79

| **TOTAL SAMPLE** | **1,660-2,771** | **59.9** |

Woodbine's numbers were comparably low on Friday, March 8th. But that was not an isolated incident. From Sunday, Feb. 3 through Monday, Feb. 11, 194 of 697 horses raced on Lasix at Woodbine, 28.0 percent, a much lower percentage than American harness tracks at the same time.

Why?

Lasix had been allowed in Canada in 1991. "I said it when the program began; Lasix is an American thing," Dr. Michael Weber, the Director of Veterinary Services of the Canadian Pari-Mutuel Agency, said in April, 2002.

A Week at Woodbine

Date	Number	Percentage
Sunday, Feb. 3	19-103	18.4
Monday, Feb. 4	24-98	24.5
Thurs, Feb. 7	27-97	27.8
Fri, Feb. 8	32-100	32.0
Sat, Feb. 9	26-91	28.6
Sun, Feb. 11	20-106	18.9
TOTAL	194-697	27.83
TOTAL SAMPLE	1,854-3,468	53.46

Amassing the numbers is easier than explaining them. Why do Standardbreds use significantly less Lasix than Thoroughbreds in North America?

Dr. Lawrence Soma of the University of Pennsylvania's School of Veterinary Medicine co-authored two significant studies of Standardbreds, one in 2000 showing that Lasix improves the performances of pacers, and, one in 2002 comparing EIPH in Thoroughbreds and Standardbreds which produced surprising results. Both studies were published in the *Equine Veterinary Journal*.

In the 2000 study with Dr. Eric Birks, Cornelius Uboh, Laura May, Donna Teleis and Joli Martini, Soma examined 769

Standardbred pacers who competed in 8,378 races between April and November, 1997, at Pocono Downs, a harness track in Pennsylvania. The pacers — 358 geldings, 270 fillies and mares and 141 horses — were administered Lasix intravenously four hours before race time. The dose was between 100 to 500 milligrams as then specified by the Pennsylvania Racing Commission.

Soma reported that 32.5 percent of the pacers who began the 1997 season raced with Lasix. The study found that Lasix "significantly decreased" race times, with the most pronounced effect being on geldings. The decrease in racing times was most pronounced in young pacers.

Citing a 1998 study by Soma and Uboh which indicated the lack of a connection between reduction in racing times and the elimination or reduction of pulmonary hemorrhaging, the 2000 Standardbred study concluded, "The decrease of pulmonary pressure produced by furosemide is not significant in magnitude to prevent hemorrhage. This would suggest that the changes in running times are unrelated to any change in pulmonary hemorrhage and that the effects of furosemide on performance are non-specific. This disconnection makes it difficult to defend the administration of pre-race furosemide, when an overwhelming concern of the racing industry is to maintain a level playing field and not encourage the use of medication which can influence performance."

Given that Soma's 1990 study had shown Lasix to improve performance in Thoroughbreds, it was not shocking to learn Lasix improved Standardbreds, too.

But a new study of EIPH in 250 Standardbreds and 250 Thoroughbreds done by Soma and Birks produced startling results. The study was scheduled to be published in the fall of 2002.

"The perception was that EIPH was believed to be less severe in Standardbreds," Soma said. "Standardbred trainers give furosemide less. The results were a surprise to us."

135

The study was done by post-race endoscopic examination of horses to determine the effect of pre-race administration of furosemide on EIPH in both Thoroughbreds and Standardbreds.

The results showed that, "There was no difference between the breeds as to the incidence of bleeding. Both Standardbreds and Thoroughbreds were found to have the same incidence and severity of bleeding regardless of whether or not they had received pre-race furosemide. This was a surprising result in the Standardbreds, as previous studies reported a lower incidence of bleeding in this breed. It has been assumed that the lower incidence of bleeding in the Standardbred was a reflection of the lower use of furosemide."

Soma's 1990 study, showing that Lasix improved performance in Thoroughbreds, elicited howls of protest from Thoroughbred horsemen who were unwilling to give up Lasix and unable to address the consequences of its usage.

But the 2002 study shows that Standardbreds bleed just as often and just as much from EIPH as Thoroughbreds. If that is true, then why do twice as many Thoroughbred trainers use Lasix than Standardbred trainers?

That won't be popular with Thoroughbred trainers either.

"I had felt for years that Standardbreds have just as high cardiac output and just as high blood pressure as Thoroughbreds," Soma said. "They're working just as hard."

There are various theories explaining why Lasix is used more frequently on Thoroughbreds than Standardbreds. They include the comparable sturdiness and temperament of the two breeds; the speed they travel; the way they warm up before a race; the position their heads are in while they racing, and the forces in the lung produced from the impact of the legs hitting the ground, a Standardbred's pace or trot compared to a Thoroughbred's gallop.

Lou Mettinis had a highly successful career training Standardbreds from 1958 to 1990, and since then has trained Thoroughbreds. "Thoroughbreds are a lot more high-strung," Mettinis said in April, 2002. "The Standardbred is a more relaxed horse, not as hyper."

Ebby Gerry, Jr., the president of the Harness Racing Museum and Hall of Fame and vice-president of the Hambletonian Society, has an interesting perspective. His aunt, Martha Gerry, raced three-time Thoroughbred Horse of the Year Forego in the mid-'70s. "Thoroughbreds are a very fragile animal, much more fragile than trotters," Gerry, Jr., said.

Trainer Don Swick, who campaigned top two-year-old pacing filly Cam Swiftly in 2001, said of Thoroughbreds, "They don't use as much aerobic training to get their lungs going. I just don't think that they have that long-distance build-up compared to the miles we put in with our horses."

It's a valid point. On the evening a Standardbred races, he will do two training miles before he steps on the track in the post parade, then jog another mile before actually racing. It's a much different pre-race regimen than that of Thoroughbreds, who basically warm-up before a race by jogging after the post parade.

There is not a significant difference in speed between a Thoroughbred and a Standardbred during a race. Top Thoroughbreds travel about 37.5 miles per hour; top Standardbreds about 32.5.

However, Standardbreds are near full-speed following the starting gate when the race begins. Thoroughbreds are standing still and accelerate to top speed in an incredibly short span of seconds. Does that added stress contribute to exercise-induced pulmonary hemorrhaging?

There is some evidence to support that hypothesis. Dr. Joe O'Dea noted, "EIPH is rare in heavy draft horses, but it is observed more frequently in pulling contests, stump removal and other endeavors which require the animals to repeatedly jerk their load forward in a to-and-fro rocking motion."

Thoroughbreds obviously don't rock back and forth, but they must expend considerable energy jerking their loads, the jockey and whatever weight is in the horse's saddle, when they go from zero to 30 miles per hour in a matter of seconds.

Swick knows one thing which certainly does not help either breed. "Our Olympic athletes when they train, they go up in the mountains," Swick said. "How many train in New York City, Chicago or Baltimore? People never think about that. We (harness horses) get that limestone that's thrown up from the track. Think of a horse with nostrils extended with nothing to protect him. It gets in their lungs and it burns. Limestone has a burning quality to it. All these horses race on limestone, especially in the East. I really do believe the air these horses breathe is a problem. You wouldn't see any other athlete doing their training while breathing this kind of air."

Equine athletes don't have a choice.

Chapter 17

Lasix is Everywhere; Uniformity Is Not

The wisdom of blanket usage of Lasix on Thoroughbreds is debatable. Lasix's presence in Thoroughbred racing is not.

A 2001, three-part, week-by-week survey of more than 48,000 Thoroughbred starters who were three-year-olds and up at 26 racetracks across America produced remarkably similar results.

In Sample 1 of more than 20,500 starters, 92.6 percent were on Lasix. In Sample 2 of more than 15,500 starters, 91.7 percent were on Lasix. In Sample 3 of more than 11,800 starters, 92.8 percent were on Lasix.

That provided a total sample of 48,128 starters, of which 44,443 were on Lasix. That is 92.34 percent. That is not an opinion, rather the reality of Thoroughbred racing in the United States. It is not the 75 percent or 80 percent commonly tossed about, but more than 92 percent.

What will that percentage be in five years if nothing is done now?

Thoroughbreds on Lasix, 2001 — Sample 1

Track	Dates	3YO & Up	Percentage
Aqueduct	Feb. 28-Apr. 14	1,827-2,098	87.1
Bay Meadows	April 4-April 15	557-563	98.9
Delaware	April 7-April 14	309-342	90.4
Fair Grounds	Feb. 26-Mar. 26	1,747-1,860	93.9

Thoroughbreds on Lasix, 2001 — Sample 1 cont.

Track	Dates	3YO & Up	Percentage
Golden Gate	Feb. 28-Apr. 1	1,431-1,462	97.9
Gulfstream	Feb. 26-Mar. 4	1,314-1,460	90.0
Hialeah	Mar. 17-Apr. 1	1,033-1,159	89.1
Keeneland	April 6-Apr. 14	425-452	94.0
Laurel	Feb. 28-Mar. 25	1,293-1,371	94.3
Oaklawn	Feb. 28-Apr. 14	2,918-3,168	92.1
Pimlico	Mar. 28-Apr. 1	915-956	95.7
Santa Anita	Feb. 28-Apr. 15	2,177-2,296	94.8
Sportsman's	Mar. 26-Apr. 14	1,017-1,165	87.3
Turfway Park	Feb. 28-Apr. 5	2,057-2,199	93.5
TOTALS		19,020-20,551	92.55

Thoroughbreds on Lasix, 2001 — Sample 2

Track	Dates	3YO & Up	Percentage
Arlington	June 13-June 24	735-790	93.0
Bay Meadows	May 23-June 23	548-558	98.2
Belmont Park	May 23-June 24	1,455-1,682	86.5
Calder	May 24-June 24	1,459-1,637	89.1
Churchill Dns	May 23-June 24	1,780-1,853	96.1
Delaware	May 21-June 24	1,413-1,625	87.0
Hawthorne	May 21-June 10	433-475	91.2
Hialeah	May 21-May 22	81-105	77.1
Hollywood Pa.	May 23-June 24	1,528-1,609	95.0
Lone Star	May 23-June 24	1,849-2,032	91.0
Monmouth	May 26-June 24	1,599-1,738	92.0
Pimlico	May 23-June 24	1,533-1,610	95.2
TOTALS		14,413-15,714	91.72

Thoroughbreds on Lasix, 2001 — Sample 3

Track	Dates	3YO & Up	Percentage
Arlington	July 4-29	1,411-1,507	93.6
Belmont	July 4-22	808-923	87.5
Calder	July 2-29	1,088-1,195	91.0
Churchill	July 4-8	372-389	95.6
Delaware	July 2-29	1,291-1,452	88.9
Del Mar	July 8-29	622-636	97.8
Ellis Park	July 11-29	1,153-1,203	95.8
Hollywood	July 4-15	575-589	97.6
Lone Star	July 3-15	797-882	90.4
Louisiana Dns	July 4-29	1,064-1,140	93.3
Monmouth	July 4-29	1,320-1,391	94.9
Pimlico	July 4-7	200-216	92.3
Saratoga	July 25-29	309-340	90.9
TOTALS		11,010-11,863	92.80
TOTAL SAMPLE		**44,443-48,128**	**92.34**

Source — Simulcast Weekly

Every state that allows Lasix to be administered to Thoroughbreds has its own rules and guidelines. Most states, but not all, specify the allowable dosage. One which does not is Kentucky, which also allows conjugated estrogens to treat bleeders and has different rules for its Standardbreds. Kentucky Standardbreds are allowed a maximum of 5 cc (250 milligrams) of Lasix up to four hours before race time.

Most states specify the time window before a race when Lasix must be administered. Other states do not. Most specified the route of delivery, either intravenously (IV) or intramuscularly (IM). Some do not.

Pennsylvania and Michigan ban Lasix for two-year-olds. Both states also call for direct oversight of the administration of

Lasix to a horse by the racing commission veterinarian or an inspector.

With the present system, the same horse racing "on Lasix" could have received 1 cc. (50 milligrams) in New Jersey and 10 cc (500 milligrams) in Florida or New York. Six of 32 states with Thoroughbred racing don't even specify a dose range for that same horse "on Lasix."

How do you handicap that?

On the day of the 2002 Illinois Derby, April 6, at Sportsman's Park, One Tuff Fox, a three-year-old trained by Richard Dutrow, Jr., was scratched for violation of an Illinois medication rule Dutrow said he knew nothing about. One Tuff Fox, owned and bred by Italo-Erin Stables, was scratched after security personnel at the track found the horse unattended after receiving a shot of Lasix. Under Illinois rules, horses who receive Lasix must be accompanied at all times by a stable employee on the backstretch. The reason One Tuff Fox was alone? His groom was taking a shower.

"We didn't know anything about this rule," Dutrow told the *Daily Racing Form*. "I've been around the racetrack since I was a little kid, and my father and brother and I have raced in New York, Maryland, New Orleans, New Jersey and Delaware, and no one has that rule. We think we were treated unfairly."

The horse's owners were considering taking legal action after the incident.

And there are actually people who think national, uniform medication rules are not a good idea?

Here's a look at the variance on state drug rules for just one drug: Lasix.

Alabama: 3 to 5 cc., up to 4 hours before post time, no route
Arizona: 2 to 5 cc., 4 hours, either route
Arkansas: 5 cc. maximum, 4 hours
California: 5 cc. maximum, 4 hours, IV
Colorado: 5 cc. maximum, 4 hours, IV or IM
Delaware: 2 to 10 cc., 3 to 3 1/2 hours, IV

Florida: 3 to 10 cc., 4 hours, IV

Idaho: 5 cc. maximum, 4 hours, no route

Illinois: 3 to 5 cc., 3 3/4 to 4 1/4 hours, no route

Indiana: 5 cc. maximum, 4 hours, IV

Iowa: 5 cc. only, 4 hours, IV

Kentucky: No dose, no time, no route for Thoroughbreds only

Louisiana: No dose, 4 hours, no route

Maryland: No dose, no time, no route

Massachusetts: 3 to 5 cc., 4 hours, IV

Michigan: No Two-Year-Olds, 3 hours, maximum of .25 mg per lb., IV or IM

Minnesota: 3 to 5 cc., 4 hours, IV under direct oversight of the racing commission veterinarian

Nebraska: Maximum of 250 mg, 4 hours, no route

New Hampshire: 5 cc. maximum, 4 hours, no route

New Jersey: 1 to 10 cc., 4 hours, IV

New Mexico: 2 to 5 cc., 3 hours, IV

New York: 5 to 10 cc., 4 to 4 1/2 hours on track grounds, IV

Ohio: 2 to 5 cc., 4 hours, IV

Oklahoma: 3 to 5 cc., 4 hours, no route

Oregon: Maximum of 5 cc., 4 to 5 hours, no route

Pennsylvania: No Two-Year-Olds, no dose, no route, no time, must be witnessed by commission veterinarian or an inspector assigned by him

South Dakota: 3 to 5 cc., 4 hours, no route

Texas: No dose, 4 hours, IV

Virginia: 3 to 10 cc, 3 hours, no route

Washington: 3 to 10 cc., 4 hours, no route

West Virginia: 10 cc. maximum, 4 hours, IV

Wyoming: 5 cc. only, 4 hours, no route

Source — The National Thoroughbred Racing Association

In Ontario, Canada, Lasix is allowed in a dose of 3 to 5 cc., 3 3/4 hours to 4 1/4 hours before post time, intravenously.

Chapter 18

Two-Year-Olds, Too?

The states of Pennsylvania and Michigan prohibit the use of Lasix on two-year-olds. Maryland banned Lasix for two-year-olds until 1992. New York considered such a ban in 1996 and bailed out.

At the other end of the spectrum are Kentucky and California.

A two-part, week-to-week sample of 3,206 two-year-old Thoroughbred starters at 16 different racetracks in the United States in 2001 showed a great variance of percentages — except for California and Kentucky.

In California, Hollywood Park had 89.2 percent of two-year-old starters on Lasix in one sample and 77.8 in the other. Del Mar had 88.5 percent in its lone sample. Bay Meadows checked in at 80.0 percent, though the sample size was just 20 horses.

In Kentucky, Churchill Downs came in at 80.5 percent in the first sample and 84.0 in the second. Ellis Park's lone sample was 79.1.

No other track with a minimum of 10 two-year-old starters was higher than 58.3.

Maybe the California and Kentucky tracks' numbers wouldn't seem so high if Delaware Park's two samples weren't 24.3 percent and 47.5; if Belmont's samples weren't 37.1 and 34.4 percent; and if one of two samples from Calder in Florida — where it is just about as hot as anywhere in the United States in May and June — wasn't 37.4 (the other was 55.8).

But they were.

Even the total sample percentage of 55.83, which included the racetracks in Kentucky and California, pales when compared to the individual numbers of those two states.

Why do 37.4 percent of 305 two-year-olds at Calder require Lasix from late May through late June, while 80.5 percent of 221 two-year-olds at Churchill Downs used it in the exact same time frame?

Two-Year-Old Thoroughbreds on Lasix, 2001 — Sample 1

Track	Dates	2-Year-Olds	Pct.
Arlington	June 13-June 24	9-32	28.1
Bay Meadows	May 23-June 23	16-20	80.0
Belmont Park	May 23-June 24	33-89	37.1
Calder	May 24-June 24	114-305	37.4
Churchill Dns	May 23-June 24	178-221	80.5
Delaware	May 21-June 24	17-70	24.3
Hawthorne	May 21-June 10	2-16	12.5
Hialeah	May 21-May 22	8-24	33.3
Hollywood Pa.	May 23-June 24	137-176	77.8
Lone Star	May 23-June 24	118-210	56.1
Monmouth	May 26-June 24	22-53	41.5
Pimlico	May 23-June 24	41-80	51.2
TOTALS		695-1,296	53.62

Two-Year-Old Thoroughbreds on Lasix, 2001 — Sample 2

Track	Dates	2-Year-Olds	Pct.
Arlington	July 4-29	57-120	47.5
Belmont	July 4-22	45-131	34.4
Calder	July 2-29	251-450	55.8
Churchill	July 4-8	63-75	84.0
Delaware	July 2-29	41-102	40.2
Del Mar	July 8-29	100-113	88.5
Ellis Park	July 11-29	121-153	79.1
Hollywood	July 4-15	66-74	89.2
Lone Star	July 3-15	81-139	58.3
Louisiana Dns	July 4-29	76-141	53.9
Monmouth	July 4-29	71-137	51.8
Pimlico	July 4-7	6-8	75.0
Saratoga	July 25-29	38-76	50.0
TOTALS		1,016-1,719	59.10
TOTAL SAMPLE		1,790-3,206	55.83

Source — Simulcast Weekly

Not all the people who question the wisdom of using Lasix on two-year-olds live in Pennsylvania and Michigan. "If you give Lasix to all the young horses, you don't know which ones are bleeders," French trainer Andre Fabre said.

Stan Bergstein, executive vice-president of Harness Tracks of America, and Claiborne Farm's Seth Hancock have trouble with the concept. "I don't understand how people can get the idea that horses that are two-years-old are inflicted with great bleeding problems and need Lasix," Bergstein said.

Hancock, speaking as the recipient of the 69th Honored Guest of the Thoroughbred Club of America, Oct. 15, 2000, alluded to attending a two-year-old maiden race full of first-time starters at

Keeneland: "There'll be ten two-year-olds in there. None of them has ever run. You look at the program. Eight of them are on Lasix. I don't understand that. None of these horses has ever run, so how could they have bled in a race? And if they bled in a workout, aren't these two-year-olds trying to tell their trainers that they're not ready to go over there and face the man? I think they're crying out for more time, and I wish we could listen to the horse and give him a little more time; take a little bit more care of him."

Hancock's suggestion makes sense to John Gosden, who has trained Thoroughbreds in Southern California and in England. "At that age, they should be rested and given a chance to come back," Gosden said. "Their lung tissue could be delicate. It might not be ready for the stress of racing. It is still a baby and it shouldn't be put on as strong a drug as Lasix."

The opposite of pampering two-year-olds would be pushing them to go ridiculously fast fractions, in the spring no less, to up their selling price at two-year-olds in training sales.

Preparing for Keeneland's April 17, 2002, Select Two-Year-Olds In Training Sale, and aided by what Glenye Cain of the *Daily Racing Form* called "gusty tailwinds," a Touch Gold filly worked three furlongs in :32 4/5, April 10. That same day, two other two-year-olds worked a quarter of a mile in :20 4/5. On turf, a filly by Theatrical worked two furlongs in :21. All told before the sale, 83 two-year-olds had a one-furlong work under :11 and 17 others worked two furlongs under :22. Were they on Lasix?

"Horses are allowed to breeze on Lasix, but last year none did," Geoffrey Russell, Keeneland's Director of Sales, said. He said medication information on this year's two-year-olds wouldn't be compiled until after the sale.

Whether free of Lasix or not, should two-year-olds be pushed to work so hard so early in their two-year-old season?

Hancock says no: "When I look down and see a horse that's not even biologically two-years-old go an eighth of a mile in :10 and change, or a quarter of a mile in :21 and change, I can't understand that. I think that's putting way too much stress on an awfully young horse. I wish the people that handle the two-year-olds would be a little more sensible about things and maybe just back off a little bit.

"I was talking to Fred Seitz not long ago, and Fred told me he had run a survey, he and his son, Joe. And they had come up with a statistic that it took 11 months on average for a horse that went through the two-year-old sale to actually make the races. That tells me that, in those two-year-old sales, we're putting far too much physical and mental stress on these horses."

New York trainer Rick Schosberg agrees. "They've been put through the ringer physically a lot more than they should be at that stage," Schosberg said. "In February and March sales, most of them aren't actually two years old. Their bones haven't hardened and set themselves. You get horses going out in :21, galloping out in :34 in February. That's like sending my nine-year-old kid to run the Boston Marathon. It's going to ruin them."

If they're doing it on Lasix, isn't that even worse? At least some people are concerned about it.

On Jan. 18, 2002, the Ocala Breeders' Sales Company sent out a "Change in medication policy effective February 2002" to all area veterinarians for its four annual two-year-olds in training sales.

The new policy eliminated the use of furosemide, as well as procaine penicillin, and disallows the use of the bronchodilator clenbuterol within 72 hours of a two-year-old's pre-sale workout.

"The main reason we did this was that under conditions of sale, there is wording referring to bleeders," Tom Ventura, general manager of the OBSC, said, March 29, 2002. "Bleeders are announced at the time of sale. We didn't want to get into a situation where a horse was given Lasix, and there was a post-sale problem because it wasn't announced. We just said we won't allow Lasix period."

Ventura said he believed less than five percent of OBSC's two-year-olds were treated with Lasix in previous years. "It wasn't

149

that big of an issue," he said.

On the same day OBSC announced its medication policy change, Fasig-Tipton announced it would restrict the use of clenbuterol, an action also taken by the Barretts Sale Company. Barretts instituted a 72-hour withdrawal time for clenbuterol before workouts at its two-year-olds-in-training sales, but took no action on Lasix. Gerald McMahon, Barretts President and General Manager, said, "Lasix is such a common medication in California."

Should it be that common everywhere?

Schosberg is not an anti-Lasix purist. He uses the drug on most horses that he trains. "I think, like any other therapeutic drug, it's got to be used intelligently and not abused," he said. "You have to realize what Lasix actually does on a cellular level. There are positive effects for racing, but also what you're doing is, you're dehydrating the system and you're dropping the osmotic pressure at the cellular level. I think what you really want to do as soon as possible after the race is re-hydrate the horse's system with not only water, but with electrolytes and minerals and vitamins."

Are two-year-olds ready for that? "In this day and age, it's kind of hard to say that two-year-olds don't bleed," Schosberg said. "There's a big push to get two-year-olds to the races, and I think that's kind of a detriment. Two-year-olds are pushed so hard to get to the races. The breed is so delicate. It is harder to keep a race horse sound in 2002 than it was in 1992. No doubt about it. I can't tell you why. We've had to train them a lot easier than we trained them. The surfaces haven't changed or only gotten better anyway. I think the breed itself has gotten soft. I don't know if it's because we're breeding more unsound horses. It's much tougher now to keep a horse sound."

Buzz Tenney, long-time assistant of trainer Shug McGaughey, said of Lasix, "There's a place for it. I think it's probably an abused drug. It's certainly an overused drug. If two-year-olds need it, maybe they need time off, in a perfect world. But that's just not going to happen these days."

Here's what happened in New York.

Shortly after New York State joined every other racing state in America by allowing Lasix, September 1, 1995, a broad band of support for prohibiting its use in two-year-olds prompted the New York State Racing and Wagering Board to propose a rule change to do exactly that.

According to its rule change proposal, the State Racing and Wagering Board would prohibit the administration of the drug furosemide (Lasix) on race day to horses younger than three years old "in order to insure that the younger horses are given the opportunity to properly develop ... The ban is necessary to safeguard against overmedicating. By increasing the age of the horse (allowed to receive Lasix), the Board is assuring that young horses prone to respiratory infection are not racing untreated as the use of furosemide (Lasix) often masks such symptoms."

In a Regulatory Impact Statement, the State Racing and Wagering Board laid out its case:

"The ban of furosemide (Lasix) on two-year-old horses would be more humane in protecting the health and welfare of these young horses.

"It has come to our attention since promulgating the rule (allowing Lasix) that the incidence of true bleeders in younger horses is less than that in older horses. Two-year-old horses have a much greater incidence of respiratory infection which can have associated coughing and bleeding on endoscopic examination. These symptoms can easily be confused with the 'true bleeders' condition. Thereby a two-year-old horse would possibly be treated with furosemide unnecessarily when, in fact, antibiotics should be used. This could be life threatening or at least detrimental to the horses. Consequently, the ban alleviates the problem of young horses unnecessarily receiving furosemide. Additionally, by increasing the age of the horse, the Board is assured that the young horses have the opportunity to mature and thus more accurately ascertain whether they need the medication."

In its legalistic language, the Board had proposed one of the oldest adages in horse racing: "Do right by the horse."

On March 12, 1996, less than 6 1/2 months after Lasix was approved in New York State, the New York State Racing and Wagering Board approved a proposed amendment to make two-year-olds ineligible for the race-day administration of Lasix.

On May 31, 1996, the Racing and Wagering Board sent a Notice of Intent to Propose a Rule, accompanied by the supporting documentation, to the Governor's Office of Regulatory Reform.

"There was a ton of opposition from the horsemen," former Racing and Wagering Board member Ben Liebman, said. "The Governor's Office of Regulatory Reform said it had little chance of passing."

So it died. And two-year-olds have continued to run on Lasix in New York ever since.

And like almost every statistic about Lasix use anywhere, the number of two-year-olds racing on Lasix in New York is steadily increasing, as is the percentage of winners of two-year-old races using Lasix.

In fact, both percentages have risen every single year since Lasix was allowed. Given enough time, New York will catch up to California and Kentucky.

Two-Year-Olds on Lasix in New York

Year	Starters	Pct.	Race Winners	Pct.
1996	608-2,546	23.9	74-291	25.4
1997	967-2,760	35.0	127-321	39.6
1998	976-2,527	38.6	145-290	50.0
1999	1,268-2,640	48.0	167-309	54.0
2000	1,353-2,607	51.9	178-304	58.6
2001	1,388-2,343	59.2	181-279	64.9

Source — New York Racing Association

Chapter 19

Lasix Cocktails

The debate over Lasix has been going on for more than a quarter of a century. But that dialogue addresses Lasix as if it was the only medication being given to a horse, as if it was administered in a vacuum. Of course, it is not.

Lasix and Butazolidin can be used in tandem at racetracks in California, Indiana, Massachusetts, Minnesota, New Hampshire, Oklahoma, Washington and West Virginia, despite concerns about Lasix's ability to dilute Bute, possibly making it undetectable in drug testing, which were first expressed more than 25 years ago.

Bute, of course, is just one of hundreds of drugs which could be used in conjunction with Lasix.

A 1990 study looked at several of them.

Ten researchers in the Race Track Division of Agriculture Canada in Ottawa examined Standardbred mares who were administered, intravenously, either 150 or 250 milligrams of furosemide and a host of other drugs to see if furosemide diluted those drugs in plasma and/or urine sufficiently to potentially interfere with detection of those drugs.

In plasma, furosemide significantly reduced the plasma concentration of codeine for two to six hours after furosemide was administered. Furosemide, however, did not alter concentrations of theyphylline, phenylbutazone, pentazocine, guaifenesin and flunixin. The data from three other drugs, acepromazine, clenbuterol and fentanyl, "were insufficient to state with certainty whether or not furosemide affected the plasma concentrations of those three drugs."

In urine, there was a "significant reduction" in the concentration of guaifensein, acepromazine, clenbuterol, phenylbutazone, flunixin, fentanyl and pentazocine within one to four hours of furosemide administration. The urinary concentrations of theophylline remained reduced for as long as eight hours after furosemide injection. Furosemide administration to horses pre-treated with codeine resulted in depression of urinary concentrations up to 12 hours after furosemide administration.

The study found that the lower dose of 150 milligrams of furosemide produced changes in drug urinary excretion and plasma elimination equivalent to the higher dose (250 mg).

The study concluded, "It is evident that furosemide affects the urinary and plasma concentrations of other co-administered drugs, but not in predictable fashion, which limits the extrapolation of these results to as yet untested drugs."

In effect, nothing had changed from 1976, when a study detailed Lasix's effect on concentration levels of Bute in urine.

How can any person in racing say Lasix does not have the potential to interfere with drug testing?

It helps if you at least know which drugs are being used.

Having completely ignored bettors by failing to acknowledge which horses were on Lasix in the 1970s, the Maryland Racing Commission took a step toward making amends in early 2002, becoming the first state to instruct its racetracks to note the increasingly popular use of adjunct medication being used with Lasix on horses. Track programs in Maryland began using a capital "A" for adjunct medication adjacent to the capital "L" used for Lasix.

According to Matt Hegarty's story in the *Daily Racing Form*, March 7, 2002, Kentucky and Louisiana also allow the use of adjunct medication with Lasix.

Those adjunct medications are aminocaproic acid,

tranexamic acid and carbazochrome, which is commonly called "Kentucky Red" on the backstretch. The first two medications are blood-clotting agents. Carbazochrome is used to treat high blood pressure.

In the *Racing Form* story, Alan Foreman, the president of the Thoroughbred Horsemen's Association, downplayed the adjunct medication's ability to enhance performance when used with Lasix. "I don't think there's any scientific evidence that it helps at all," Foreman said. "Just some people on the backstretch think that it does a little bit of good."

Who gets to decide what constitutes on a "little bit of good," and who gets to make wagers knowing that information?

But what does Lasix do when it's used in combination with the early 2000's "now" medication, the bronchodilator clenbuterol? On January 30, 2002, the California Office of Administrative Law approved a proposed rule passed by the California Horse Racing Board, November, 30, 2001, allowing clenbuterol to be used in that state.

Clenbuterol is widely accepted as an effective therapeutic medication, but at least two studies questioned the efficacy and potential danger of using clenbuterol in conjunction with Lasix.

In a study published in the December 2000 issue of the *Journal of Veterinary Pharmacology and Therapeutics*, four researchers (M. Manohar, T. Goetz, P. Rothenbaum and S. Humphrey) from the University of Illinois at Urbana-Champaign College of Veterinary Medicine tested clenbuterol to see if using it in conjunction with Lasix would reduce EIPH. They concluded that it did not, saying, "Clenbuterol administration is ineffective in modifying the pulmonary hemodynamic effects of furosemide in standing or exercising horses. Because the intravascular force exerted onto the blood-gas barrier of horses pre-medicated with furosemide remained unaffected by clenbuterol administration, it is believed that concomitant clenbuterol administration is unlikely to offer additional benefit to healthy horses experiencing EIPH."

But could administering clenbuterol and Lasix be dangerous to the horses that are treated with them?

Dr. Kenneth McKeever and Charles Kearns of the animal sciences department at Rutgers University, did separate long-term studies of clenbuterol and delivered their results at the American College of Sports Medicine's annual 2001 meeting.

"We were looking at the effects of chronic administration, which has been explored by owners in Kentucky about giving it to young horses," McKeever said. "One of the suggestions is to put two-year-olds on clenbuterol. It's something we see in practice out there, both in Thoroughbred racing and, if they can afford it, for horses in equestrian events. Both are using clenbuterol to treat respiratory disease. If you do that, you can reduce plasma volume, which reduces fluid that produces sweat, thus decreasing cardiovascular and thermal stability.

"Lasix is a diuretic. One of the effects of Lasix is to get rid of a tremendous amount of fluid in the body. So the horse has to compensate by moving fluid from other compartments, cells or the space in between the blood stream and cells, making the cardiovascular system work harder. They think it improves performance. We found the opposite.

"Based upon the results of our studies, you're going to compound things (by using clenbuterol and Lasix). You have a horse who already has a decreased plasma volume and dehydrate it more. You run the risk of many problems, the potential to not thermal regulate (keeping the horse cool because of less sweat), overheating and risk of thermal injury, such as heat stroke or heat exhaustion in humans. Theoretically, it could happen in horses."

Kearns warned, "Using clenbuterol in conjunction with Lasix, you are dehydrating your animal to dangerous levels. You are forcing the kidneys to work harder. These are health risks that trainers and veterinarians should start thinking about."

McKeever suggested a prudent course of action: "Research is needed to study chronic use of clenbuterol and Lasix."

Imagine that: Studying the effects of medication before permitting its blanket usage. The racing industry's past performance lines say that was a policy which was left at the gate a long, long time ago.

Chapter 20

Alternatives

It's a funny thing about alternatives. You have to look for them to find them. Preserving the status quo is a much easier, more traveled path.

Having never been involved in horse racing, scientist Richard Blackmer of Klamath Falls, Oregon, did not know the status quo of treating bleeding racehorses with furosemide. In the mid-1980s, he found another way to treat them.

Blackmer worked for General Electric in Schenectady, N.Y., for 25 years, conducting membrane technology research in fields as diverse as deep-sea diving and the Gemini Space Program.

In 1976, he and Jon Hedman formed the Oxygen Enrichment Company and developed a high-humidity, oxygen-enrichment machine to aid people with cystic fibrosis, a fatal disease which is the nation's No. 1 genetic killer of children and young adults.

Cystic fibrosis slowly takes over a child's body by not allowing the normal production of free-flowing secretions necessary to remove mucous and bacteria. The secretions are produced by the endocrine gland and are vital to bodily functions such as breathing and digestion. Cystic fibrosis victims produce abnormally thick secretions which allow mucous to accumulate in various parts of the body, particularly the lungs and intestines.

The common therapy, which is repeated twice daily, is technically called chest physiotherapy. Actually, doctors, therapists and/or parents literally whack a child's chest to free mucous trapped in the lungs.

Blackmer's high-humidity, oxygen-enrichment machine facilitates the removal of mucous-filled excretions.

"The theory is basically humidic," Blackmer explained. "We're using pure, completely filtered water vapor."

He had no idea there could be an equine equivalent to his invention which could aid bleeders. "When we got into horse racing, I had never heard of exercise-induced pulmonary bleeding," Blackmer said. In fact, he hadn't even been to a racetrack until March, 1985.

His 25 years of experience with membrane technology research led him to a rather obvious conclusion about EIPH. "We can't make the horse better than he is, but we can remove the impediments that prevent him from getting his full oxygenation," Blackmer said.

Those impediments include the typical poorly-vented environment a horse lives in at the racetrack. "Every horse is in a barn with dust, fungus, pollen and pollution," Blackmer said.

People who smoke in the barn only make a bad breathing environment worse.

To combat that environment, Blackmer devised an equine adaptation of his high-humidity, oxygen-enrichment machine and called it an Equine Transpirator.

"Transpiration is changing liquid water to vapor through a membrane," Blackmer said. "The machine filters air through a pretty high-grade inlet filter. The air is then run into a transpirator device. The air is delivered to a heated, partially-insulated flexible plastic tube to a nasal muzzle mask. A thermocouple in the tube determines the temperature. What we're doing is cleaning out mucous. In polite society, it's called pulmonary hygiene."

Watching a Thoroughbred treated on an equine transpirator in 1985 — as part of a clinical experiment at Saratoga and Belmont Park in 1985 — was a revelation. The unidentified Thoroughbred,

Horse A, was a four-year-old bleeder who had finished a tiring eighth in his last start, which was a day before his transpirator treatment.

"I never thought high-strung Thoroughbreds would stand still for this machine," said Blackmer's assistant, Kevin Verdon, who trained harness horses for 12 years. "They all love it. This horse loves it."

A yellow bucket with a mask at the end of the heated delivery tube is strapped onto Horse A's nose. The horse, who looks likes his head is stuck in a bucket, stands dead still. He continues to remain absolutely motionless while Verdon connects the bucket to the tube and turns the machine on. Horse A remains placid. In just a couple of minutes, his ears sag. In 20 minutes, approximately one-fifth the time of a routine treatment, the mask is removed for a second to show what's inside. Already, the inside of the mask is spotted with dirt which had been in the horse's respiratory system.

Initial studies with the transpirator were encouraging. Dr. Lawrence Soma of the New Bolton Center at the University of Pennsylvania, and Dr. Jack Foster Harris, a veterinarian from Bensalem, Pennsylvania, were involved in an experimental study of the transpirator on 13 Thoroughbreds and one Arabian racing at Delaware Park in the summer of 1985. Twelve of the 14 horses were bleeders being treated with Lasix.

"We had seven to 10 horses I was involved with," Harris said. "The machine improved them in every case. Several times, we had phenomenal results. Some of them stopped bleeding completely."

Soma said at the time, "I don't think it's going to be a panacea, but it helps a certain number of horses."

Dr. James Belden, a noted New York Thoroughbred veterinarian, said he was aware of 14 Thoroughbreds in New York who were treated confidentially in another experimental trial in 1985. "In two cases, I've had dramatic results with it," he said at the time. "One horse had a chronic breathing problem. The other had an allergic problem, a low-grade allergy to dust. They cleaned that horse up very nicely. Another six or seven horses, it's helped significantly in terms of their performance and the diminution of post-exercise hemorrhaging. It has helped."

Endoscopic examinations were done after 34 known bleeders were treated with the transpirator in 1985: 14 Standardbreds at Saratoga, The Meadowlands, Garden State and Blue Bonnets, and 20 Thoroughbreds at Saratoga and Delaware Park. Twenty-eight of the 34 — all except six Thoroughbreds at Delaware Park — were treated on the transpirator without Lasix. After racing, they were scoped. Fourteen of the 28 known bleeders showed no bleeding. Ten showed less severe bleeding. Four had unchanged bleeding.

Six Thoroughbreds used Lasix and the transpirator and were scoped after racing. Two showed no bleeding, two showed less severe bleeding and two had unchanged bleeding.

Transpirators have apparently evolved into nebulizers. The extent of their usage and their success on the backstretches of North America's Thoroughbred and harness racetracks is not documented.

But that is only one alternative. Canadian Thoroughbred trainer Robert Rose has another, which is why he re-claimed the seven-year-old Premier's Turn in late July, 2001.

The 61-year-old Rose, who has been training since 1961, had trained Premier's Turn in 37 of his 58 career starts, the last 57 on Lasix. "I'd had Premier's Turn off and on throughout his career," Rose said in an August 2, 2001, story by Bill Tallon in the *Daily Racing Form*. "He has a severe breathing problem. All his other problems I was able to address, but his breathing has always been a concern to me. I'd tried every product on the market. Some of them helped him, but he was never cured. I became transfixed with developing a product that would help this horse. It wasn't about money. He's so game. I love the horse."

Rose had never loved Lasix. "I've had some nice horses in

164

my time," Rose said. "And I've seen what they look like after a close race with Lasix. They become dishrags."

Rose, who has a stable of 10, has a farm, Rose's Farm, in Caledon, Ontario. "It's 1,200 feet in elevation above Toronto," Rose said in an April, 2002, interview. "We don't get that same dome of bad air. Woodbine is right behind the airport. We have major highways. All these highways are in close proximity to the racetrack. Besides that, the water from Lake Ontario has been proven to have lots of pollutants. I think today we're fighting pollution. That's my biggest concern. I began, three or four years ago, focusing on what I can do to help. That's what got me interested. I did a lot of research on herbs to offset the pollution."

After much experimentation, Rose concocted a blend of organic herbal ingredients he mixes into a horse's feed. Called Vigilant, it has no chemicals nor pesticides. "No medication, zero," Rose said. "I've studied the medicinal power of plants, and I recognize the importance of organically grown herbs. I've documented which herb does what.

I'm working with a number of ingredients. One comes from France; another ingredient comes from China. I'm picking up sources, some from British Columbia, some from the southern United States."

Among the 14 herbs Rose uses in different proportions to make Vigilant are Echinacea, Yellowdock, White Oak Bark, Marshmallow Root and Calendula Flower. "Each one addresses a specific concern," he said. For example, Yellowdock is used to reduce inflammation of the respiratory tract; Marshmallow Root helps expel mucous from membrane tissues.

"Vigilant strengthens the immune function and seals leaky blood vessels by the interaction," he said. "It aids in repairing pulmonary arteries and reduces inflammation in the respiratory tract, heals nosebleeds and throat sores and protects the inner lining of blood vessels from oxidative damage."

Rose is buoyed by the fact that in August, 2000, the Equine

Research Centre of Guelph, Ontario, completed research which showed that Echi-Fend, a product developed from the herb Echinacea, was effective in horses as an immuno-stimulant and haematinic agent for horses.

Rose advises horsemen to use one scoop of Vigilant daily for 42 days added to sweet feed and grain for lunchtime feed without other supplements. He also recommends no workouts or races and light training only.

Of course, there's the distinct possibility that any Thoroughbred would benefit from six weeks off with or without Vigilant.

But in the space of a year, Rose's results have been significant enough to sell Vigilant to other horsemen and to attract an offer from Univet, a major veterinary products company in Canada. "There was a time we sold one bottle a week," Rose said. "Now I'm selling it every day."

Trainer Sheldon Wolfe, a long-time friend of Rose who has been using Vigilant on his horses, said this about Lasix: "I've never liked it, but it was essential to maintain racing. We know every trainer is not going to forego Lasix, but this gives trainers a choice."

That's only another alternative.

The Equine Pulmonary Laboratory at Michigan State University offered this alternative at its website, Sept. 1, 2001: "Another treatment being investigated involves drugs such as nitric oxide, which work as vasodilators (increasing the circumference of the blood vessels) and vascular smooth muscle relaxants allowing the blood vessels within the lungs to accommodate the large increases in blood volume that occur during strenuous exercise. If this occurs, the pressure within the vessels will decrease, and the hemorrhaging associated with EIPH should be decreased."

There are other options. Writing about bleeding in *Horsepower-Ireland*, Des Groome believes at least some incidents of bleeding are preventable:

"My experience is that a failure to diagnose minor

respiratory disease in time coupled with the tradition of running horses before they are fully fit, are the two most common Irish causes of bleeding. Major cases of EIPH are hard to spot as the lungs can clear a minor bleed in two or three hours.

"The first step in treatment involves blood sampling and Bronchial Lavage, otherwise known as a lung wash. Around 90 percent of cases are due to some underlying disease or infection. Results will pinpoint a course of treatment. Multi-factorial respiratory allergies are on the increase in horses. Rapeseed, hay moulds and wooden stables have all been noted as causes of EIPH. Management and prevention go hand in hand.

"The young horse needs to be well conditioned before racing, well vaccinated to boost the immune system and regularly spot-checked by the vet to prevent respiratory problems escalating to EIPH. The chronic bleeder will need dust-free forage and husk-free feeding, improved stable hygiene, more ventilation and a bedding change to sand, rubber or paper. The bleeder needs more training than the usual horse. A gradual climb to a higher level of fitness will prevent oxygen debt and fatigue when racing.

"Optimum fitness will hold blood pressure at its critical level and prevent burst blood vessels. In conclusion, frequently scoping after routine exercise is essential to look for early warning signs. Abrupt exercise demands and poor standards of disease prevention both lead to EIPH. The basic biological dilemma of the equine athlete is that the oxygen demands of competition produce pressure in the lungs that nature never intended. We owe it to the horse to understand and manage this dilemma."

EIPH is obviously a difficult dilemma to even understand before it can be addressed. "Bleeding is such a complex disease, process or problem," said top New York trainer John Kimmel, a former vet who does his horses' endoscopic examinations himself. "There are so many factors that go into what causes a horse to bleed. There are environment-related concerns for bleeders. There is a very close correlation between a horse's level of stress and the extent to which a horse bleeds. I think you can see when horses are under stress, and that can take many forms. For example, if you take a non-bleeder turf horse and run him on dirt, the stress of the change in surface might cause him to bleed. His efficiency of movement is decreased. He has to work harder. That might be enough to trigger the cascade.

"There are other examples. Horses that have had viruses, fever and bacterial infection are the various types that have first-time bleeding. You have to know how serious their illness has been and be very cautious as you increase their workload so that these horses show no signs of bleeding."

At its website, a livestock/feed supply company in Bel Air, Maryland, called The Mill of Bel Air offers its opinion on reducing bleeding: "The use of feed to combat bleeding may have some merit. Excess dust and/or molds in feed may be enough of a stress to weaken the lining of the lung. Use of clean, dust-free hays will help. Horses are designed to eat with their heads down (grazing). Hay offered in hay nets at head level makes it more likely that dust will enter the lungs. Therefore, hay at ground level reduces this chance. The grain mix you use depends more on your training situation than it does on having a 'bleeder feed.' Furthermore, the company offers these management tips: 1) reduce dust and mold, 2) feed hay on the stall floor and, 3) optimize anti-oxidant vitamins and trace minerals, which are important for tissue integrity and repair."

Equine teacher and instructor Laura Phelps-Bell offers these suggestions to prevent repeated episodes of bleeding: "First, if your horse is housed in a barn, make sure that there is plenty of ventilation. Exposure to fungus, mold spores and other potential allergens should be avoided, so only provide hay that is free from dust, mold and weeds. Make sure that your horse's stall is kept mucked-out to avoid possible exposures and irritation from the ammonia in his urine and bedding. If at all possible, your horse should live outside, or be turned out, for as many hours a day as possible. Second, try to feed your horse in a more natural grazing position with his head and neck lowered to eat. When fed from feeders that are above eye level, horses inhale spores and dust from their hay which irritate their airways and lungs."

It's hard to imagine that there's a downside to trying to improve a horse's breathing environment in its barn. In a January, 1992, study in the Department of Large Animal Clinical Sciences at Michigan State University by R. Slocombe, F. Derksen, P. Gray and N. Robinson, 11 horses were exposed to aerosolized ovalbumin, an agent that promotes inflammation which would be similar to a chronic allergy condition for a horse stabled in a city. Ovalbumin was administered to the horses' lungs, and five hours later the horses were exercised. Before being exercised, they were scoped and did not reveal any abnormality. After exercise, there was "extensive blood in airways leading to the exposed lung in all horses." The study concluded, "Exercise can cause blood from an injured region of the lung to appear in the larger airways. Regional differences in lung structure and function do not influence the appearance of blood in the airways."

The Lasix alternative which has generated the most amount of publicity is the Flair™ nasal strip, the equine version of the human Breathe Right strips for cold and allergy sufferers. Two former veterinarians, Dr. Edward Blach and Dr. Jim Chiapetta, invented Flair nasal strips, which are manufactured by CNS, Inc., the same Minneapolis company which manufactures Breathe Right strips for humans, and are distributed world-wide by Merial Limited.

Flair nasal strips were introduced in October, 1999, and received immediate credibility when three of the eight winners of the Breeders' Cup at Gulfstream Park, November 6, 1999, wore the four-by-six-inch, butterfly-shaped strip, which is attached over the nasal passages by an adhesive. The strip's spring tension holds the horse's nasal passages open to maximize air flow.

The three Breeders' Cup winners were huge longshots:

Cash Run at 32-1 in the Juvenile Fillies, Anees at 30-1 in the Juvenile and Cat Thief at 19-1 in the Classic. Both Cash Run and Cat Thief were trained by Hall of Famer D. Wayne Lukas, whose dominance in the Breeders' Cup has been extraordinary. His 16 career Breeders' Cup victories are nine more than Shug McGaughey in second, and Lukas also ranks No. 1 in career seconds, thirds and earnings, all by wide margins. The point is that both Cash Run and Cat Thief had been racing very poorly to be sent off at those double-digit odds and ran incredibly better that day wearing nasal strips.

Overall that day, 27 Breeders' Cup starters (28 percent) wore nasal strips.

But that very afternoon, Lukas warned about reading too much into the nasal strips, saying that he had used them simply because he thought they could not hurt and might help his horses.

Still, it was a compelling image in the winner's circle after the 1999 Breeders' Cup Classic. Cat Thief was wearing a nasal strip, and so was his jockey, Pat Day, one of many athletes who continue to use the Breathe Right human strip.

How and why does a nasal strip work for horses?

In a December 15, 2001, story in the *Thoroughbred Times*, Denise Steffanus succinctly offered this explanation:

"When a horse breathes in, it creates a vacuum that draws in the soft tissues right behind the horse's nostrils. Some researchers believe the vacuum also may suck blood out of the capillaries of the lungs, resulting in pulmonary bleeding. In theory, if the nasal passages are held open by a nasal strip, the horse will create less of a vacuum, thus limiting pressure on the capillaries and reducing exercise-induced pulmonary hemorrhage. Advocates of the nasal strip maintain that it also decreases the work of breathing."

Do nasal strips work? Lots of horsemen think they do.

By the end of 2000, nasal strips were allowed in 34 of 36 racing states in America, the exceptions being New York and New

Jersey — Pennsylvania allowed them for Thoroughbreds, but not Standardbreds.

Flair has been approved by the Federation Equestrian International, American Horse Shows Association, National Reining Association, U.S. Equestrian Team, U.S. Polo Association, National Barrel Horse Association and the American Quarter Horse Association. They are allowed in Australia (harness only), Barbados, Brazil, India, Jamaica, Korea, Mexico, The Netherlands, New Zealand, Qatar, Singapore, Trinidad and the United Arab Emirates.

But do they work? Initial clinical research was favorable. So was one of two reports since.

Initially, a study of the "Effects of External Nasal Support on the Pulmonary Gas Exchange and EIPH in the Horse"[1] involved seven healthy geldings, six Thoroughbreds and one Quarter Horse, on a high-speed treadmill. The conclusion was that nasal strips "have the potential to constrain EIPH."

"The Effects of Flair Nasal Strips on Upper Airway Mechanics in Exercising Horses"[2] was presented at the 2001 World Equine Airways Society Conference. Six Standardbreds were studied, and the conclusion was that "The Flair nasal strip decreased work of breathing in exercising horses."

At the same conference, another study was presented, "Effect of Furosemide and Nasal Strip on Exercise-Induced Pulmonary Hemorrhage in Maximally Exercised Horses."[3] Three Thoroughbreds were studied on motorized treadmills to assess the effectiveness of the nasal strip and furosemide in enhancing performance and reducing EIPH in maximally exercising horses.

[1] Poole, Dr. David, Casey Kindig, Gus Fenton, Leah Ferguson, Dr. Bonnie Rush and Dr. Howard Erickson, Departments of Kinesiology and Anatomy & Physiology, Kansas State University, *Journal of Equine Veterinary Science,* Vol. 20, No. 9, 2000

[2] Holcome, S.J., C.J. Cornelisse, F.J. Derksen and N.E. Robinson, Large Animal Clinical Sciences, Michigan State University College of Veterinary Medicine

[3] Kindig, Casey, Paul McDonough, Gus Fenton, Melissa Finley, David Poole and Howard Erickson, Departments of Anatomy & Physiology and Kinesiology, Kansas State University.

The results suggested that EIPH severity was reduced with the nasal strip and furosemide in all three horses, although furosemide appeared more efficacious.

More recently, two researchers presented contradictory papers at the American Association of Equine Practitioners annual convention in San Diego, November 25, 2001.

CNS, Inc. financed a study by Dr. Ray Geor of Kentucky Equine Research, who studied the effectiveness of nasal strips and furosemide, alone and in combination, on reducing the severity of EIPH in Thoroughbreds. The effectiveness of using neither was also recorded. Horses were subjected to a two-minute exercise session on a high-speed treadmill. Thirty minutes after exercise, the researchers performed a bronchoalveol lavage (which infuses and extracts fluid) and counted the number of red blood cells in the lavage fluid to determine the extent of EIPH. Geor reported "substantial and statistically significant declines" in red blood cells in all three trials (nasal strip alone, furosemide alone and nasal strip and furosemide), meaning a decreased severity of EIPH. Using just the nasal strip decreased severity 45 percent; furosemide only 56 percent, and nasal strip and furosemide together 68 percent. In his presentation, Geor noted that all three treatments decreased EIPH without preventing it, and that the horses' oxygen consumption was reduced using the nasal strip. He concluded, "Given the purported performance-enhancing effects of furosemide, the nasal strip does prove a viable alternative for the prophylaxis or mitigation of EIPH."

Then Dr. Gordon Baker, the chief of staff of the large animal clinic at the University of Illinois, presented the findings of his study, which was partially funded by the Illinois Thoroughbred Horsemen's Association and the Illinois Equine Research Fund. Working with his colleagues, Dr. Thomas Goetz and Dr. Murli Manohar, Baker studied how the nasal strip affected EIPH and the end product of respiration, changes in blood-gas exchange and anaerobic metabolism. "What we have measured is the end product rather than the specific mechanism," Baker said. "If the end product of anaerobic metabolism doesn't change, then it's irrelevant what it does halfway along. The lactic acidemia and the levels of Hypoxemia (oxygen debt) don't change. And if they don't change, then therefore there is no effect of the mechanism."

Baker concluded, "The fact that statistically significant differences in any of the above parameters were not observed in strenuously exercising horses following the application of the external dilator (Flair) strip raises doubts regarding meaningful benefits to its use in racehorses."

Obviously, any study of nasal strips is hindered by the fact that they've only been used since October, 1999. The debate over its effectiveness may continue for years.

But noted handicapper Andy Beyer asked a different question: Do nasal strips improve performance? Beyer did his own analysis of horses at Churchill Downs from October 31 through November 27, 1999, and concluded that, "The data from Churchill suggest that bettors can disregard nasal strips as a handicapping factor."

As a non-invasive, non-medicated breathing aid for racehorses, it cannot be disregarded as a viable alternative for Lasix. Except at the New York Racing Association's three tracks, Saratoga, Belmont Park and Aqueduct.

In late October, 1999, the New York State Racing and Wagering Board approved nasal strips for an experimental trial period at Aqueduct from its opening day, October 27, through the end of the year. A couple days later, the New York Racing Association banned their use in races, though it did not ban them for training.

NYRA CEO Barry Schwartz said the decision was made by the stewards, and NYRA Steward David Hicks explained, "We knew nothing about them, and I don't like to endorse something that the public doesn't know about, whether it affects a horse or not."

Meanwhile NYRA trainers continue to increase their use of Lasix, even on two-year-olds. We're still trying to figure out the effect of that.

Chapter 21

The Mother of All Studies

When Dr. Lawrence Soma and his colleagues at the New Bolton Center at the University of Pennsylvania showed in their 1990 study that Lasix improved performance of both EIPH-positive and EIPH-negative Thoroughbreds — besides questioning the efficacy of Lasix in treating EIPH — the study was criticized by some because of the size of the sample. Only 131 of 665 horses completed the study.

"Larry got jumped on," Soma's long-time contemporary, Dr. Thomas Tobin of the University of Kentucky Drug Testing Program, said in March, 2002. "It has turned out to be well supported. Bigger studies and more sophisticated studies have established that."

None were bigger than the 1999 study conducted by Dr. Kenneth Hinchcliff, an associate professor of veterinary medicine at Ohio State University; Paul Morley, an assistant professor of epidemiology and biosecurity at Colorado State University, Tom Wittum, an assistant professor of epidemiology at Ohio State, and Diane Gross, a graduate teaching assistant at the department of veterinary preventive medicine at Ohio State.

Entitled, "Effect of furosemide of Thoroughbreds racing in the United States and Canada," the study was published in the September 1, 1999, issue of the *Journal of the American Veterinary Medical Association*.

This sample size was the 22,589 Thoroughbreds who

competed in 3,346 dirt races at 49 tracks in the United States and Canada which allowed Lasix between June 28 and July 13, 1987. Only the first race for each horse during that time period was included. Horses that did not finish the race were not included.

Of the sample, 16,761 (74.2 percent) raced on Lasix, and 19,088 (84.5 percent) had raced on Lasix at least once.

The sample consisted of 41.3 percent females, 11.3 percent males and 47.4 percent geldings. Most horses were three or four years old, although age ranged from two to 14. Races ranged in distance from two to 14 furlongs. The most common distance was six furlongs, comprising 35 percent of the sample.

Race records were analyzed by the use of multivariable procedures and logistic regression analyses to determine the effect of Lasix on estimated six-furlong race time, estimated racing speed, race earnings and finish position. Principal component analysis was used to create orthogonal (uncorrelated) scores from multiple collinear variables for inclusion in the models. "What that means," Hinchcliff explained in an April, 2002, phone interview, was, "that because performance is really determined by so many different things, age, sex, jockey, surface, ability ... we wanted to account for as many of those factors as we could so we could identify furosemide as a factor. The mathematical analysis accounts for the effect of other factors."

The study showed that horses on Lasix raced faster; were 1.4 times more likely to win a race; 1.2 times more likely to finish in the top three, and earned an average of $416 more than the horses not receiving Lasix. The greatest effect of Lasix on six-furlong times was in males. When horses of the same sex were compared, horses receiving Lasix ran faster by the equivalent of 3 to 5.5 lengths. Lasix improved performance. "It was nice to have our results from 1990 confirmed," Soma said.

The Hinchcliff study said, "Because of the large study population and resulting statistical power, the magnitude and consistency of the observed effect, and the fact that the study population was likely representative of the population of Thoroughbred horses racing in the United States and Canada, we believe that our results present clear and unequivocal evidence of an association between use of furosemide and superior performance in Thoroughbred racehorses."

The study then explored possible explanations for the improved performance with Lasix, including the reduction in the severity of EIPH; the induction of metabolic alkalosis, and the reduction in body weight.

In dismissing the first possibility, the reduction in severity of EIPH, the study noted, "We consider it unlikely that furosemide would have exerted a performance effect through an effect of EIPH, as there is no evidence that furosemide reduces the prevalence of EIPH in Thoroughbred racehorses. There is also little objective evidence that it reduces the severity of EIPH or that EIPH has a negative effect on the athletic ability of horses except in the rare case of horses with severe or catastrophic bleeds."

Regarding the second possibility, the induction of metabolic alkalosis, the study said, "Induction of metabolic alkalosis improves athletic ability of some human athletes, and furosemide has been shown to induce alkalosis that persists during incremental exercise and during brief, high-speed exercise similar to that performed in a race. However, a performance-enhancing effect from furosemide-induced alkalosis has not been demonstrated in horses."

The study then addressed the possibility of weight reduction, noting that furosemide has been shown to induce a two to four percent reduction in body weight within four hours. "Because work is a product of mass, velocity and distance, and given the acknowledged importance of weight carriage when handicapping Thoroughbred racehorses, it would be expected that loss of this amount of weight would have a beneficial effect on athletic ability of furosemide-treated horses," the study said. "This contention is supported by reports that the furosemide-induced reduction in body weight increases the maximal rate of oxygen consumption, reduces the accumulated oxygen deficit and apparent rate of lactate production, and decreases the rate of carbon dioxide production of horses during intense exercise. These effects, which are prevented by carriage of weight equal to the loss as a result of furosemide administration, are considered indicative of a performance-enhancing effect of furosemide."

The study continued, "Many extraneous factors may influence the performance of a racehorse, but these factors are often highly correlated. Principal component analysis is a type of multivariate analysis that uses matrix algebra to create orthogonal (uncorrelated) scores from correlated variables. It was useful in the present study because it allowed all available information from the original variables to be included in the analysis despite the collinearity of these variables. This allowed us to control as many other sources of variation as possible. In this manner, we could be more confident that observed differences in performances of horses were associated with administration of furosemide. When the principle component scores were not included in the model, furosemide administration was still associated with superior performance; however, the magnitude of the effect was less. Inclusion of the principle component scores in the model allowed us to develop more refined estimates of the effects of furosemide on the performance of Thoroughbred racehorses."

The study concluded: "Because of the pervasive use of furosemide and its apparent association with superior performance in Thoroughbred racehorses, further consideration of the use of furosemide and investigation of its effects in horses is warranted."

Reacting much quicker than it did to the 1990 study suggesting Lasix enhances performances, the American Association of Equine Practitioners fired a pre-emptive strike against the 1999 Hinchcliff study. Noting the Hinchcliff study was to be published, Sept. 1, 1999, the AAEP made a statement Aug. 28, 1999. AAEP President Dr. Robert D. Lewis said, "The AAEP welcomes research into this much-debated area of equine veterinary medicine; however, we urge all participants in the racing industry to recognize that differences of opinion do exist regarding conclusions drawn from this data," Lewis said.

Here's the conclusion the AAEP reached in its policy statement: "In support of veterinary treatment in the best interest of the horse, the AAEP maintains that: Horses that experience EIPH should receive appropriate veterinary care; Furosemide is currently the most effective therapeutic medication available for the treatment of EIPH; and increased scientific research regarding EIPH will provide improved treatment options and the greatest benefit to the health and welfare of the horse."

That scientific research the AAEP hungered for was in the study it chose to ignore.

By 2001, more than 92 percent of Thoroughbreds in the United States were racing on Lasix.

179

Chapter 22

Truth or Consequences

On the fourth of December, 2001, the racing industry in the United States took an unprecedented step forward as part of the University of Arizona's annual Race Track Industry Program's Symposium on Racing.

At a Racehorse Medication Summit fashioned by the Association of American Equine Practitioners, 34 representatives of horseracing got together in a single room and spent nine hours behind closed doors trying to work together, first in a two-hour briefing by experts on topics that would be considered, and then in an intense, seven-hour workshop. Represented were, in alphabetical order: the American Quarter Horse Association, the Association of Racing Commissioners International, the American Association of Equine Practitioners, the California Thoroughbred Trainers Association, Churchill Downs, Harness Tracks of America, the Horsemen's Benevolent and Protective Association, the Jockey Club, the Kentucky Thoroughbred Association, the National Thoroughbred Racing Association, the Thoroughbred Horsemen's Association, the Thoroughbred Owners and Breeders Association, Thoroughbred Owners of California, Thoroughbred Racing Associations, the Thoroughbred Racing Protective Bureau, the United States Trotting Association and the United Thoroughbred Trainers Association. Also attending were two trainers, Richard Mandella and John Ward, Dr. Ron Jensen from California and Dr. Rick Sams from Ohio State University.

They agreed to pursue a uniform direction.

Unfortunately, the direction they chose calls for eliminating all-race day medication except furosemide. "Because bleeding can become a fairly serious problem, currently the only medication with scientific evidence of helping that condition is Lasix," Dr. Jerry Black, the President of the American Association of Equine Practitioners, said in February, 2002. "It decreases the severity of bleeding. Until we have something coming down the pike that is more efficacious, we feel Lasix is our only choice."

That's not good enough.

If furosemide gets grandfathered in now, racing in North America will never be rid of its dark shadow and all the questions Lasix brings, questions which have never been answered, even while Lasix use has increased to embrace more than 92 percent of our Thoroughbreds in its three decades of use and mis-use.

"It's so entrenched in North America," Dr. Kenneth Hinchcliff of Ohio State University said. "Everybody expects to use it."

Then we must change expectations.

A dose of reality would be a start.

And one reality is that not every horse using Lasix needs to use Lasix.

Asked if it's a good thing to see 11 or 12 two-year-olds in a 12-horse maiden race on Lasix, Gary Biszantz, Thoroughbred Owners and Breeders Association Chairman of the Board and a long-time California owner and breeder, responded, "I don't think it's a good thing, and I don't think it'll be a good thing if clenbuterol becomes an accepted drug and all 12 horses run on clenbuterol. I don't think that's a requirement. In other words, I think medication should be used when it's necessary. It's like when someone's sick, they need to go to a doctor. You need medical help when you've got something the matter with you. But if you're perfectly healthy, you don't need to have that medication in you just because the fella in the stall next to you has it, and the one in the next stall does, in other words just because you're trying to compete with the next guy."

Another reality is that Lasix does not stop bleeding.

"There is good evidence that Lasix does not prevent bleeding, but a lot of people give Lasix believing that it does," Dr. Warrick Bayly of Washington State University said in a January, 2002 phone interview. "I think it's still a prevailing opinion, not just of veterinarians, but of horses owners and trainers, that administering it prevents EIPH. I think there's strong statistical evidence that horses run faster when they are given Lasix. What it comes down to is why, and is that bad? It's a very controversial issue. I don't have any definitive opinions because I don't think definitive evidence that's required to make a conclusion exists."

What do we know?

We know that it took some 15 years to get Lasix use documented in a track program; nearly 20 years to get the information included in a horse's past performance lines in the *Daily Racing Form*, and that we've used Lasix for more than 30 years without answering the questions that will not go away.

Does Lasix affect performance? Of course it does, for some horses.

Does Lasix stop bleeding? It does not.

Does Lasix diminish bleeding? Absolutely, for some horses.

Does Lasix mask or flush other drugs? The debate on that is more than 30 years old and no closer to resolution than it was when Lasix was introduced.

Yet trainers and owners and breeders in North America continue to use Lasix in increasing numbers, even on two-year-olds, who may not be able to handle such a strong medication. The number of those horsemen without at least a concern about the mis-use and over-use of Lasix is a minority.

The Race Track Industry Program at the University of Arizona, in conjunction with that historic Racehorse Medication Summit, Dec. 4, 2001, did a medication survey of owners, trainers and veterinarians. Respondents were not required to sign their names with their responses, giving them a rare chance at honest commentary protected by anonymity.

In his Dec. 16, 2001, column in the *Daily Racing Form*, Steve Crist printed the results and re-printed some of the comments.

Seventy-eight percent of the owners who responded said there is a medication problem in racing, and 94 percent characterized it as moderate or severe, rather than slight. One owner wrote, "It's obvious that some stables are using illegal drugs. When trainers win at a 30 percent clip, claim horses for $5-$15K and routinely win allowance races with them, it makes the playing field very uneven. It also chases the honest owners out of the game."

Another owner wrote, "Is there a drug problem in New York? You bet there is. Since Lasix has been allowed, claiming horses is a nightmare ... Lasix is not the problem, it's what it hides and what is not being tested. There is way too much painkillers (not Bute) and hormones used today. When a vet says you can't win unless you pay $700 per horse per month, something is very, very wrong. I only hope something will be done before I lose everything."

Of the trainers who responded, 73 percent thought there is a medication problem, and 64 percent characterized it as moderate or severe. One trainer wrote, "If a trainer is a 'big name,' everyone is looking to absolve them of responsibility. There is always a lead time when trainers, usually big trainers, get away with using 'new' drugs that do not show up in the tests. When they are caught, do they get a serious penalty? The news media always runs to their defense — how about being concerned about the trainers running second and third and fourth to these medicated horses? It's always said, 'Well, they are a really successful trainer; why would they cheat?' Well, maybe that's how they got successful."

A different perspective was offered by Daniel Warrington, a harness trainer for over 30 years in Galena, Maryland, in a letter to the editor of *Mid-Atlantic Thoroughbred Magazine* following an

184

article about integrity in racing:

"Everyone is looking to the integrity of the trainer, or the integrity of the driver or the jockey. How about looking at the integrity of the owners in both of our industries (Thoroughbred and Standardbred)? I realize that most horse owners — although they are the most important component in our industries — are not usually hands-on daily participants. This, however, does not excuse them from turning a blind eye to any unethical practices that may be going on with their animals. I believe that any medication ruling that results in a suspension should go against the trainer of the horse and the owner. I realize this is placing a huge burden on the owner. However, you can't deny that it would go a long way in cleaning up both our sports."

Many Thoroughbred trainers who use Lasix do so half-heartedly.

"Lasix is a necessary evil," New York trainer Gary Contessa said. "Until they approve a better drug, Lasix is a necessity."

Hall of Fame New York trainer Phil Johnson, said of Lasix, "I think it's a good product. It's a safe product. Nobody ever said it stops bleeding. It lowers the blood pressure and allows the horses to breathe normally under high stress. If it masks drugs, then don't allow it. That I agree with."

Gasper Moshchera, New York's leading trainer for six consecutive years from 1993 to 1998, said much in New York has changed since Lasix was permitted on Sept. 1, 1995. "They (other trainers) dilute drugs so they can't find them," he said. "It's like chemistry warfare. It's not training."

Hall of Fame California trainer Neil Drysdale said, "My feeling is that as much as Lasix can definitely control bleeding, I think, that at present, until a better drug comes along, which I think it will, Lasix is the drug of choice."

It is not everybody's choice. Not in Australia, England, France, Ireland, Germany, Japan, the United Arab Emirates and dozens of other countries.

185

Perpetuating North American horses' drug dependency by allowing race-day Lasix is a policy which will seal our horses' fate.

The Great Lasix Lie was that it was going to heal our Thoroughbreds and allow them to make more starts and have longer careers. In fact, the exact opposite has happened.

Can Lasix impact the breed? Dinny Phipps, Chairman of the Jockey Club, thinks it already has. "I do think it has impacted the breed," he said. "We have some horses who would not have reached the level of performance they reached that have the same problem. That is supposition and that is not fact, but it's what I feel."

He's not alone. "All medication has impacted the breed since the '70s," Lauren Stich, the pedigree columnist for the *Daily Racing Form*, said. "We're breeding very fragile horses. The horses we're treating with Lasix and other medications are becoming our stallions. We're breeding unsoundness. That's why horses aren't making as many starts."

TOBA's Biszantz said, "Horses are not running as much as they used to run. We were led to believe that if we used more therapeutic medication and helped the horse more, he would be able to run more. So the facts are starting to show clearly that that's not occurring. I don't know if it's all medication's fault, but it certainly has something to do with it."

Hinchcliff, who calls furosemide "a remarkably safe drug when used as directed in racehorses," nonetheless wonders if there will be repercussions: "Are we selecting for breeding a population of horses that are some way dependent on the continued use of furosemide?"

A commentary in the Fall, 1999, issue of *Equine Canada* said, "The widespread use of race-day medication could be creating a gene pool requiring drugs to perform."

Are there alternatives? Yes.

Is there another way to go besides uniform addiction to this powerful diuretic? Yes there is. If we look around, we even see people pointing in the right direction. The states of Pennsylvania and Michigan which do not allow two-year-olds to race on Lasix. The Hambletonian Society which has been banning Lasix, as well as Bute, from harness racing's premier trotting classic, and its filly counterpart, for more than a decade.

Why can't the leaders of Thoroughbred racing at least agree that the sport's best races, the Breeders' Cup and other Grade 1 stakes, should be run medication-free? There will be no catastrophe, just as there is no catastrophe when America's best horses ship to Dubai and race without Lasix.

"If you we're going to clean up, so to say, any bias related to medications, you would probably want to make your Grade 1 races no-medication," New York trainer John Kimmel said. "Those are the horses who become the major contributors to the gene pool. In the long run, you might want to have something to say about keeping bleeder-free horses as the main breeders."

Start with Grade 1 stakes. Do that the first year. Then extend it to all graded stakes the next. Then to all stakes.

Why can't racing's industry leaders agree that two-year-olds should not be racing on Lasix? It is virtually unused in harness racing's two-year-old Breeders Crown races. Why can't harness racing's leaders extend that to all two-year-old races? Why can't Thoroughbred racing do the exact same?

Do something.

Not a person in the industry is suggesting eliminating the use of Lasix as a valuable medication for bleeders.

Except on race day.

They should be drug-free on race day just as they are in almost every major racing country in the world except the United States and Canada.

And deep down, most horsemen and officials know that.

Hall of Fame trainer Allen Jerkens has been training in New York for 52 years. Until 1995, there was no race-day Lasix. "We didn't have Lasix, and I think we were doing all right," he said. "I have a good friend of mine, a trainer. He runs every horse on Lasix.

He does well. He said Kelly's Kip (a multi-stakes winning sprinter trained by Jerkens) would have done really well with it. I said, 'He ran in 1:07 and three.' I said, 'How fast would he have gone, 1:06 and four?' We were just kicking it around."

Jerkens does use Lasix on some of his horses. "It has its merits," he said. "You get the odd horse that it helps. It makes them lighter. I had horses in my lifetime who would urinate a lot after the race. I always said to myself, 'If he had done this before the race, he would have been better off.' Now people use it because everybody else is. That's what it's become. I could get along without it."

So could our horses.

About the Author

Bill Heller, a freelance writer in Albany, N.Y., won the 1997 Eclipse Award, the 1999 William Leggett Breeders' Cup Award and a 2001 and 2002 first place in the American Horse Publications Awards for magazine writing about Thoroughbred racing. He is a three-time winner of the John Hervey Award for magazine writing about harness racing. He writes regularly for the *Thoroughbred Times*, *The Backstretch*, *Mid-Atlantic Thoroughbred* and *Canadian Sportsman*. This is his 14th book.

Selected Bibliography

• Arthur, Rick M., DVM, "Furosemide: Practice and Politics," *American Association of Equine Practitioners Proceedings*, 1990

• Bosken, J.M., T. Tobin, G.D. Mundy, M. Fishcer and R.O Banks, "Comparison of Specific Gravity and Osmolality in Post Race Urine of Furosemide-Treated and Control Thoroughbred Horses," in *Proceedings of the 13th International Conference of Racing Analysts and Veterinarians, Cambridge, UK*

• Chay, Sylvia, William E Woods, Kim Rowse, Thomas E. Nugent, J.W. Blake and Thomas Tobin, "The Pharmacology of Furosemide in the Horse. Pharmacokinetics and Blood Levels of Furosemide After Intravenous Administration," *The American Society for Pharmacology and Experimental Therapeutics*, Vol II, No. 3, 1983

• Chay, S., W.E. Woods and T. Tobin, "The Pharmacokinetics and Blood Levels of Furosemide After Intravenous Administration," *Proceedings, 5th International Conference Cont Use of Drugs in Race Horses, Toronto, Canada*, June, 1983

• Combie, Joan, MSc, Thomas Nugen and Thomas Tobin, "Furosemide, Patella Vulgata B-Glucuronidase and Drug Analysis: Conditions for Enhancement of the TLC Detection of Apomorphine, Butorphanol, Hydromorphone, Nalbuphine, Oxymorphone and Pentazocine in Equine Urine," *Research Communications in Chemical Pathology and Pharmacology*, Vol 35, No. 1, January, 1982.

191

• Combie, Joan, MSc, Thomas Nugen and Thomas Tobin, "The Pharmacology of Furosemide in the Horse. The Duration of Reduction of Urinary Concentration of Drugs," *Journal of Equine Veterinary Science*, 1:203-207, 1981

• Cook, W. Robert, FRCVS, PhD, *Specifications For Speed in the Racehorse: The Airflow Factors*, The Russell Meerdink Company, Ltd., Menasha, WI, 1993

• Erickson, H.H., DVM, PhD, C.A. Kindig, MS, D.C. Poole, "Exercise Induced Pulmonary Hemorrhage: A New Concept for Prevention"

• Gabel, Albert A, DVN, MS, Thomas Tobin, DVM, PhD, Richard S. Ray, DVM, MS, PhD and George A. Maylin, DVM, MS, PhD, "Furosemide in Horses: A Review," June, 1977

• Gross, Diane K., DVM, Paul S. Morley, DVM, PhD, DACVIM, Hinchcliff, Kenneth W., BVSc, PhD, DACVIM and Thomas E. Wittum, MS, PhD, "Effect of Furosemide on Performance of Thoroughbreds Racing in the United States and Canada," *Journal of the American Veterinary Medical Association*, Vol. 215, No. 5, September 1, 1999

• Harkins, J.D., Wyndee Carter, C.G. Hughes and Thomas Tobin, Editors, "Furosemide in the Horse. Its Actions, Effects, and Regulatory Control. A Testing Integrity Program Seminar," March 1, 1998

• Hinchcliff, K.W., BVSc, MS, PhD, "Management and Pharmacotherapy of Exercise-Induced Pulmonary Hemorrhage in Horses," World Equine Airways Society (WEAS), 2001

• Hinchcliff, Kenneth W., BVSc, PhD, DACVIM, "Effects of

Furosemide on Athletic Performance and Exercise-Induced Pulmonary Hemorrhage in Horses," *Journal of the American Veterinary Medical Association*, Vol. 215, No. 5, September 1, 1999

• Holcombe, C.J. Cornelisse, F.J. Derksen and N.E. Robinson, "The Effect of Flair Nasal Strips on Upper Airway Mechanics in Exercising Horses," WEAS, 2001

• Kindig, Casey A., Paul McDonough, Gus Fenton, Melissa R. Finely, David C. Poole and Howard H. Erickson, "Effect of Furosemide and Nasal Strip on Exercise-Induced Pulmonary Hemorrhage in Maximally Exercising Horses," WEAS, 2001

• Kindig, Casey A., Paul McDonough, Gus Fenton, David C. Poole and Howard H. Erickson, "Efficacy of Nasal Strip and Furosemide in Mitigating EIPH in Thoroughbred Horses," *Journal of Applied Physiology*, 91:1396-1400, 2001

• Langsetmo, I, M.R. Fedde, T.S. Meyer and H.H. Erickson, "Relationship of Pulmonary Arterial Pressure to Pulmonary Hæmorrhage in Exercising Horses," *Equine Veterinary Journal* (2000)

• Miller, J. Richard, B.L. Roberts, J.W. Blake, R.W. Valentine and Thomas Tobin, "Drug Interactions in the Horse," *Research Communications in Chemical Pathology and Pharmacology*, Vol 17, No. 3, July 1977

• O'Dea, Joseph C., DVM, *The Racing Imperative*, The Castlerea Press, Geneseo, NY, 1998

• Pascoe, John R., BVSc, PhD, Dipl. ACVS, "Exercise-Induced Pulmonary Hemorrhage: A Unifying Concept," *American Association of Equine Practitioners Proceedings*, Vol. 42, 1996

• Poole, David C., PhD, Casey A. Kindig, MS, Gus Fenton, MS, Leah Ferguson, BS, Bonnie R. Rush, DVM, MS and Howard H. Erickson, DVM, PhD, "Effects of External Nasal Support on Pulmonary Gas Exchange and EIPH in the Horse," *Journal of Equine Veterinary Science*, Vol. 20, No. 8, 2000

• Roberts, Brian L, B.Sc, J.W. Blake, PhD and Thomas Tobin, DMV, PhD, "Drug Interactions in the Horse: Effect of Furosemide on Plasma and Urinary Levels of Phenylbutazone," *Research Communications in Chemical Pathology and Pharmacology*, Vol 15, No. 2, October, 1976

• Roberts, Brian L, B.Sc, J.W. Blake, PhD and Thomas Tobin, DMV, PhD, "The Pharmacology of Furosemide in the Horse. Its Detection, Pharmacokinetics, and Clearance From Urine," April 1978

• Shultz, Ted, Brian L. Roberts, Jerry W. Blake and Tomas Tobin, "The Detection, Identification and Basic Pharmacology of Furosemide in the Horse"

• Slocombe, Ron, "EIPH: The Role of Airways." WEAS, 2001

• Soma, L.R., VDM, L. Laster, PhD, F. Oppenlander, VDM and V. Barr-Alderfer, PhD, "Effects of Furosemide on the Racing Times of Horses with Exercise-Induced Pulmonary Hemorrhage," *American Journal of Veterinary Research*, Vol. 46, No. 4, April 1985

• Soma, L.R. and C.E. Uboh, "Review of Furosemide in Horse Racing: Its Effects and Regulation," *Journal of Veterinary Pharmacolog. Therapy*, 21: 228-240, 1998

• Sweeney, Corinne Raphel, Lawrence R. Soma, Cynthia A. Bucan and Susan G. Ray, "Exercise-Induced Pulmonary Hemorrhage in

Exercising Thoroughbreds: Preliminary Results with Pre-Exercise Medication," *The Cornell Veterinarian*, Vol 74, No. 2, July, 1984

• Sweeney, Corinne Raphel, DVM Lawrence R. Soma, DVM, Abby D. Maxson, DVM, Joseph E. Thompson, BA, Susan J. Holcombe, BS and Pamela A. Spencer, ScM, "Effects of Furosemide on the Racing Times of Thoroughbreds," *American Journal of Veterinary Research*, Vol 51, No. 5, May 1990

• Tobin, Thomas, DVM, PhD, Brian L. Roberts, BScm T.W. Swerczek, DVM, PhD and Mark Crisman, "The Pharmacology of Furosemide in the Horse. Dose and Time Response Relationships, Effects of Repeated Dosing, and Performance Effects," *The Journal of Equine Medicine and Surgery*, May 1978

• Tobin, Thomas, David S. Watt, Stefan Kwiatkowski, Hwin-Hsiung Tai and Jerry W. Blake, "Non-Isotopic Immunoassay Drug Tests in Racing Horses: A Review of Their Application to Pre- and Post-Race Testing, Drug Quantitation, and Human Drug Testing," *Research Communications in Chemical Pathology and Pharmacology*, Vol 62, No. 3, December, 1988

• Tobin, Thomas, MVB, MSc, PhD, MRCVS, *Drugs and the Performance Horse*, Charles C. Thomas, Springfield, IL,

• Tobin, Tom, DVM, PhD, "Furosemide (Lasix(r)) in the Horse: An Overview Presented to the 23rd Annual Convention of The American Association of Equine Practitioners"

• Wood, T., C.L. Tai, P. Henry, W.E. Woods, T. Tobin, S. Wie, C.A. Prange, J.McDonald, R.J. Ozog and M.T. Green, "The Detection of Furosemide in Equine Blood by Fluorescence and Enzyme-Linked Immunoassays," in *Proceedings of the 7th International Conference of Racing Analysts and Veterinarians, KY*, 1988

Index